Woman of Many Names

Woman of Many Names

Debra S. Yates

Total Fusion Press
Strasburg, OH

WOMAN OF MANY NAMES

Total Fusion Press
6475 Cherry Run Rd., Strasburg, OH 44680
www.totalfusionpress.com

Printed in the United States of America
25 24 23 22 21 20 19 18 17 16 1 2 3 4 5

ISBN (paperback): 978-1-943496-07-5
ISBN (hardback): 978-1-943496-08-2
Library of Congress Control Number: 2016948086

Edited By: Jamie White
Cover Design By: Jamie White

Published in Association with Total Fusion Ministries, Strasburg, OH. www.totalfusionministries.org

Dedication

To my mother JoAnn Yates, whose blood line and cultural influences made me the woman I am.

Acknowledgements

I would like to thank Brent Yates and my entire family for their love and support. Also much thanks goes to my chosen sisters: Sandi Berry, Julie Navratil, Barbie Ludwig, Vicki Knapp, KC Temple, Carol Dekkers, Dawn Fisher, Jeri Dunlap-Wood, Lorraine Cocker, Jan Roberts, and Barbara Dunlap.

Table of Contents

Her Many Names

Tsistuna-gis-ke':	Original birth name
Wild Rose:	Childhood nickname
Nanyehi:	Name from ages 10-19 years old
Nan-the-hi	Translation: "One who walks with the Spirits"
Ghighau:	Name from ages 19-death
War Woman of Chota:	Title given by the Cherokee chiefs
Beloved Woman:	Translation of Ghi gh u
Greatly Honored Woman:	Title
Cherokee Rose:	Legendary Nickname
Nancy Ward:	American name given after marriage to Bryant Ward
Chiconehla:	Translation of Nancy in Cherokee
Granny Ward:	American nickname in later years
Nani:	Cherokee grandchildren called her
Pocahontas of Tennessee:	Legendary Nickname

Foreword

As a woman born into a Cherokee Nation in the 18th century, I should have known by the way I came into this world that my life path would be painful as well as full. I have long awaited the time to share this story and life path with my seven times great granddaughter, Debra S. Yates. However Debra did not know that the path she would walk would be as long and painful as mine. My granddaughter Debra carries the same spirit as me. The spirits that watched over and guided me now bring their guidance to her and keep her safe on her journey of life. Together, Debra and I will weave a story that I began sharing with her at the Overhill, in the land of the Cherokee, overlooking the Ocoee River in Benton, Tennessee.

Preface

At the age of twelve I discovered my ancestry.

I praised the Creator for showing me the beautiful story of my great grandparents. Their story has been scarcely addressed in our North American History, yet I have such immense pride in my Cherokee ancestry that it must be told.

As a curious child I began to question my Grandfather Buffington Tittle of his life on, what he called, the Reservation in Oklahoma when he was a child. Locking his stories in my mind throughout the years, I had the pleasure of meeting several of my Oklahoma relatives who took joy in recanting stories they had been told by their parents as young children. Little did I know that one day I would be the one to retell their stories that had been shared within my family for many generations.

I began to write my seventh great-grandmother Nancy (Nanyehi) Ward's story to further explain her part of American history. She helped to sculpt this country I love. It is a story of tremendous courage and love. It is also a saga of a destiny foretold and fulfilled by a woman of the greatest honor amongst her people, the Cherokee. This is the legend of a woman who wanted to keep her people and children safe in a world that was changing with a speed that could not be controlled. Undeniable forces came together through this era of history. North America was being invaded by countries from all over the world, monarchies and diocese thirsty to seek and possess the treasures of a new fertile land. With these forces came the demise and destruction of many indigenous people of America. Great men and women of American History walked the lands during Nanyehi's lifetime. Many of whom she encountered personally and others she knew only through the power of negotiations. She knew of infamous men we only know of from history lessons, like George Washington, Thomas Jefferson, and Daniel Boone. Nancy Ward sat on numerous influential treaty counsels and many land transfers. She worked tirelessly to ensure her children, grandchildren, and those who followed this ancestry would have a place to call home in today's society.

As I tell the story of a girl born as Wild Rose - the woman who was declared by the US government as the last princess and prophetess of the Cherokee Nation - my hope is that more people come to understand and appreciate this marvelous woman's place in American history. Though she was a great warrior and lead her people to great victories over those that would destroy her land and her children, my great-grandmother is remembered as a great peacemaker in her culture. She was a woman who risked the wrath of her own people to protect them from invaders and each other. Nanyehi had the ability as a medicine woman to heal, to glimpse into the future and to make decisions that would affect her as well as that of the invaders of her lands. Many generations of settlers of this wild and dangerous country owe their very lives to this miraculous woman. These are the words of my seventh great-grandmother. Her words rang with simple yet all-encompassing truth that still rings true today. I have written this book that none of us forget where we came from and what we owe this land, the land that holds the blood of our ancestors.

Introduction

After my birth in the capital of the Cherokee Nation, Chota, I was named *Tsistuna-gis-ke*. Some moons later they began to call me *Wild Rose*, a name chosen by my mother as she thought my cheeks had the coloring of the petal of the roses that grew wild in our valleys and meadows. Just before my sixth year, I became known as *Nanyehi*: One who walks with Spirits! This was a high honor in the large tribe of the Cherokee Nation and put a large burden upon me as I was so young: a burden no one could understand.

After the Battle of Taliwa and the death of my first husband, Kingfisher, my people bestowed upon me the honored name of *Ghighu*: Beloved Woman. There were those that called me *War Woman of Chota* or *Greatly Honored Woman*. After my marriage to Bryant Ward my name became *Nancy Ward*, which became my American name. There were some who also referred to me as *Cherokee Rose*. But regardless of all the names given throughout my lifetime, the names I loved the most were Mother, Nani or Granny Ward.

The many names were carried for many reasons that are clear. But with the passing of time it became difficult for others to understand. Weaving together the past of my family one would have to know the many names that we carried and the purpose for those names. Our people understood but those from other lands and cultures did not. There were those that called me princess, prophetess, Chieftainess, War Woman of Chota, and Greatly Honored Woman, and then there were those that called me traitor. I became a woman of *many* names for *many* reasons. These words are sent through the smoke of time to my many grandchildren and to all those that would seek to know my story.

Understand, my grandchildren, that through the veins of you and your seed run the blood of many great warriors, braves, healers and chiefs. Know that where one drop of my blood runs so am I also there. My children were all born of love: those that lived and those that did not. My heart beats for the love of my many children that were born of my womb and others' wombs; the love of my People runs deep. As America looks back into its past I pray they will see that our native ways were not those of evil heathens that did not deserve to live , but as protectors of the land our Great Creator put us upon and commanded my people to love, respect and care for. Our People have worked tirelessly to ensure a place in this land for the sakes of our children, and of their children, and the children of the future. They are all the seeds of my soul and of those whom have come before.

We, the Cherokee, are known as the Original People- the Magic People of the Smoking Mountains. We were admired for our skills at war, skills in hunting and success as negotiators. We also possess the ability to heal with the medicines taught and given by our Creator. These medicines are brought forth from the flowers of the fields and the bark of the trees and the roots of many plants. The simple dandelion that grows freely everywhere is used in its entirety, from the flowers and the stems to the very last of their roots. We are taught to take only what is needed, to use all that is given, and not waste any gift given by the Creator. The Ancient Ones have long told the stories by the fire how the Creator put us upon this land first. He put us in

13

charge of the lands which we live upon. He entrusted the Cherokee people with keeping his land safe and clean.

My many grandchildren, you are the Original People, Ani-Yuawia, the Water People of the Wolf Clan, Kituwah protectors, you are Cherokee, the magic people. You are the ones that have descended from Great Chiefs, Warriors and Peace Makers. We all have a need to know the future and strive to preserve the past.

I send this through the smoke of time, a story of a *Woman of Many Names*.

Wild Rose

It was a bitterly cold morning within the shadows of the Great Smoking Mountains. The Nunnehi, Little Spirit People, were busy with their fires beneath the mountains. Kati, my mother had been laboring for two days and was heavy with a child that was reluctant to come into this world.

The medicine man, Atawehi, stayed close to the village awaiting the birth of Chief Moytoy's grandchild. For these past days he had spent much time watching over the progression of this long difficult labor. He recited poems and sang songs to the unborn child boy, and, when the child boy did not come forth, he then began reciting the poems and singing songs to the unborn child girl.

Our medicine men have studied long and are taught in the ways of our ancient medicine people. They are taught by their fathers who learned from their fathers. All has been passed down through the smoke of time by our ancient healers. They are taught the mixtures of the many herbs, barks, flowers and roots. Our Atawehi study long so they know best how to heal our people. We believe in keeping our bodies in the right way as not to become ill. Some healers are chosen by the old ones of our tribe. Some are born with the knowing of the Ancient Atawehi, and there are those that are passed from father to son.

My grandparents Moytoy and SuGi lived in Great Tellico, not far from the village of Chota where I was born. My mother moved with her twin brother Attakullakulla and their other brother Oconostoa. They moved to Chota to start their own town. Grandmother SuGi traveled to our town close to the time Kati was to give birth. She was alone without the protection of her husband, ~~Fivekiller, who had been killed in a battle protecting and defending the life of her father~~, Chief Moytoy. Great Tellico was the place where my mother and her many brothers had been reared.

Kati had been laboring for such a long time that she had grown very tired and weak as the hours went by. The medicine man mixed a potion of dogwood bark, ginger and coneflower, and brewed a healing tea for her that SuGi helped her drink. This eased her pain for only a short time. After the day had passed the small one was still showing no signs of being ready to be born. When the evening came he once again seeped a tea for her to drink, only this time he added coral root to the tea. The coral root is used sparingly as it is a strong pain medicine.

SuGi worriedly paced the area, for her daughter had been laboring long and hard, and she worried for her daughter and her unborn grandchild. When the time became right she helped my mother bear down and bring forth her child. Her anxious face turned to glee as she heard the newborn wail. SuGi began to ready the infant for a journey to the Little Tennessee River for the ritual newborn bath. The Atawehi tried his best to dissuade her from taking the young one for such a cold bath, but she refused. She assured him that this baby's spirit was special and must be raised by custom because her spirit had been foretold to her in a dream vision. This child was to become a great leader amongst the People. Her spirit would be guided by the Great Shepard and the Ancient Ones. After the Atawehi had finished caring for Kati he left Chota and headed to Great Tellico to inform my grandfather of my mother's health and of the child's birth.

All of our family was sad that my father had not lived to see me be born to the world. My father was called Chief Fivekiller whom married my mother and left the Bird Clan to join my mothers' clan the most honored people of the Cherokee Nation, the Wolf Clan. Ours is the clan from where many great chiefs and leaders were born, because it is the only clan from which one was able to take the life of a wolf spirit. Only members of our clan or descendants of our clan had this right.

My mother suffered much pain at the loss of my father so close to my birth. By custom she was not allowed to speak his name for a full year. Cherokee custom could also keep her from marrying again for four years if the council so choose. Yet though she had the right within twelve full moons to take another husband from that of the Bird Clan - the clan of my father- she never did. As we grew older she would tell my older brother Longfellow and I that our father was enough, that he left his spirit here in their two children. My brother was four when our father passed from this world and has said many times that he has no memory of him. Mother often told us that Longfellow had the look of his father and many of my ways were like that of my father. Never would mother say if this was good or bad.

Grandmother SuGi went to the river to bathe and pray to the Creator for my life in this world. She parted the skins in which I was wrapped and sprinkled me with water instead of dipping me into the river as this was the coldest day that even the old ones could remember: November 19, 1738. As she made her way up the sloping banks of the Little Tennessee River returning to my mother's longhouse, she was suddenly halted in her tracks. There SuGi was greeted by a large, male white wolf that loomed over my grandmother and I at the crest of the bank. My grandmother vowed an oath that morning to the Great White Wolf, the most honored of all wolves. SuGi swore that I would be raised in the way of our People and would be trained to fulfill my destiny, one that he revealed to her that early winter's morning.

My grandfather, Chief Moytoy, whom the English King George II had proclaimed the Emperor of the Cherokee Nation, was patiently awaiting word of the birth of his daughter's second child. Kati held a special place in her father's heart. He knew her spirit was still heavy with grief from the loss of her husband so near the birth of his newest grandchild. He understood well her loss. As the Chief of the Cherokee Nation during the time the British and the French were sending more and more settlers to what was called "the new land," he had seen much loss to his family as well as his people. He also felt much guilt over his daughter's husband's death, for FiveKiller had died in his stead.

It all seems as a dream of long ago. I was in the fall of my tenth year. My cousin, Little Owl, was a young brave – not yet a warrior – and was going on a war party. I so wanted to see what he and the other braves and warriors did on these small scouting and war parties. I longed to wear the red paint and follow Little Owl and the other warriors to war. When I tried to follow along with Little Owl, he scolded me and sent me back to the village saying that there was no place for a girl on a war party.

I was sure I could follow them from a distance and prove to Little Owl and the others of the tribe that my skills could be of use on a war party. My skill set could certainly be of use: I knew the hiding places of the herbs and recognized the trees that could heal our wounded warriors. I could hunt small game for food and prepare it. Women were so dedicated to ensuring a victory for their tribe that they also were known to chew the bullets of the guns for better shooting.

So my adventure began. My plan was to follow the warriors from a distance down the trail and track them along their way. Then, perhaps, they would know of my skills and wish for me to join them.

Foolish thoughts of a young girl.

Upon the fall of darkness, I lost the trail of the warriors. I was trying to be as brave as the men, but found myself praying to the Creator to keep me safe from harm. I stopped to listen for any noise of the war party that I had been following, but no sounds of their movement could I hear. I went to the top of a mountain to try and spot any signs of a camp. None did I see. It started to become cold so I nestled in for the night.

The night grew even darker and the smoke began to rise from the mountains. I fell asleep by a log that had fallen underneath a cedar tree. The chill of night rose deep around me, but soon there was protection from the early winter's cold night as if a fur had been laid upon me. The white wolf had come to keep me warm and safe.

When the first rays of the sun spread across the top of the mountain, I awoke to find a man and woman by a nearby fire making cornbread and heating water to seep a warming tea. When the woman took notice that I was awake she motioned me to come and sit with them to share the morning meal.

We sat and ate and spoke the high language of the Ancients. Growing up in the presence of many visitors to our villages, and being the granddaughter of a Principal Chief, I was often in the presence of those who spoke the tongues of the Ancients as well as the high, middle, and the lower languages. I learned the trader language, and the languages of other tribes. I often wondered why we spoke so many tongues instead of one.

That morning the man and woman shared with me things I could hardly believe or understand and instructed me to remember everything they shared that day in the dense misty smoke that arose from the mountains. They told of stories from our past as well as our future. In me grew the planted seeds of knowledge and seeing, gifts only given to few. I had been chosen to help our people through some of the most trying times we would ever know. Having seen what I was to do through their eyes and through their thoughts, I came to understand that my life would never be my own.

When the sun had begun to warm the day and the smoke of the mountains had faded away, the man, woman and I began to walk as the white wolf took the lead in front of us. After we walked for many hours I began to see places I recognized. Then as we walked on further I saw something that was very familiar to me. I climbed upon a large boulder and could clearly see my village. Turning around I thanked the intuitive couple for bringing me home and bade them to come eat at our lodge as my mother would be happy to prepare a feast for my new friends and celebrate my return home. I was sure mother had worried about me all through the night. I spotted Little Owl crouched low by the river so I repeatedly shouted out his name until he heard my voice. He quickly sprang to his feet, waved a greeting to me and ran as the wind towards our town.

Around that time, something was being shouted throughout the village which grew louder and louder. I stood still upon the rock listening closely; I was able to clearly hear the chanting, "Wild Rose! Wild Rose!" My name was being shouted throughout Chota. I turned around to thank the kind people who had returned me to my clansmen, when the woman began to speak:

"Child of the White Wolf, you are safely returned to your mother and your people. Continue your quest for knowledge and know that whenever you are in need of us we will be there. Watch for the red bird with the black mask upon his face, he will lead you from harm's way. Study the coats of the animals, they will show you the many signs of the weather. Watch the feathers of the hawks' bellies, they will tell you when the snow will be or how much to expect. When their belly is white you will know there will be much snow. They will tell of the way of each season if you learn them. Learn the seasons and remember the signs they give. Keep your heart open to all people and watch and remember their ways. You will see many changes that will come with the smoke of time. Learn well the past and you will know the future. For as a people we are destined to repeat our past mistakes. You are loved, child, and you are worthy. Remember all you have learned for the wisdom you possess will save your people."

I watched as the man and woman disappeared into the mist of the forest. The great white wolf also made his way toward the wood's edge. As the white wolf neared the edge of the forest he stopped and, with a turn straight toward me and a howl from his soul to my spirit, he left me. I was once again by myself but the words they left with me would keep me from ever feeling alone again.

My mother was at my side swiftly asking of me where I had been. How was it I came to be with the people that she saw walking into the mist of the forest? So many people gathered around us with so many questions. Many of whom had spent the night and most of the day searching for me, a silly child who wanted to join a war party. Little Owl wanted to know where the white wolf had gone that was standing next to me on the boulder. Before I could answer him my mother lifted me gently in her arms and we headed towards home.

As we approached the edge of town I could see many of our people had gathered to greet us. All seemed to be happy that I was home. We went to the lodge of my uncle Chief Attakullakulla that was close to the center of town. I was allowed to rest after my long walk home once we had eaten a meal of venison and bread. When I awoke from my dreamless sleep it was to the elders of our tribe that had gathered outside of Attakullakulla's longhouse. They began to question me about my night lost in the woods so far from home. The trackers had followed my steps and they ended at the top of the mountain where they lost all signs of my trail.

I told the elders and my uncles and those that were gathered there all that I could remember of that night of being lost. I revealed only part of that day that I had spent with the Spirit People, because the secrets they revealed to me I knew I must keep to myself. I will always remember from the smoke of the past what they told me that day.

When I had finished telling my clan the story of my night with the spirit people and the white wolf, Attakullakula told me from this time forward, my name would be changed and I would be known as *Nanyehi* – One Who Walks with the Spirits. My uncle told me the Spirit people that lead me safely home to Chota were Nunnehi. Up to this time in my life, I thought

22

walking with spirit was something done by all. Now I knew how different I was from my people; I was one with the Spirit.

Nanyehi

After my time in the mountains when I traveled with the Spirit people, Old Water- the painter - came to our longhouse. He spent the night and ate from our cook pot with us. Early in the morning he began to mix the ink that would soon mark my arms. He took his time mixing and crushing berries that he carried in small clay pots. Porcupine needles were placed in boiling water then placed aside for him to work with. This pain I would find to be easier than other trials I would face; my new life was before me.

For the next three moons, Old Water stayed at our longhouse and told me stories of the painting of my Uncles' marks. Oconostoa and Attakullakulla were marked over most of their arms, hands, face and torso. These markings showed of their rank as Chiefs of a great Nation. The patterns explained their life stories, the wars they fought, the losses of family, and their great deeds. Through these moons my arms were marked with red paint. Old Water also painted small red dots across my nose and cheekbones. Teaching where to precisely place these markings set me apart from all in our Nation and the Nations of others. Only those of us who can see or hear the spirits are allowed to wear this kind of painted mask. Our marks are all distinct to the person they were made for by our Creator, no two are alike.

There were times these marks made my life harder and there were times these marks would save my life. With these marks upon me, there would be no place for me to hide.

In the years that followed, often the memories of walking with the Spirits would come to mind as my markings were noticed and I would reminisce with the winds of time. Some of my most fond memories as a child were times of hunting, gathering leaves, tree barks, and special herbs for a poultice or tea to be used by the Atawehi to heal the people of their wounds and sicknesses. The Atawehi work and study long under their father-teachers to learn and know well the ways of the Ancient medicine men and women. It had been decided by the Elders when I was six years old that I was to be taught the ways of the Atawehi. In me they saw the signs they look for in choosing whom to teach. This was a high honor for a girl, let alone a child of my young age. The Atawehi of Chota told me that I would be joining him to hunt the herbs and flowers. He said he was too old to bend over to harvest the plants and one as small as I, being closer to the ground, would have no trouble picking up the many herbs that he needed. The Atawehi have long known that the Great Spirit gave to us all that is needed to heal ourselves. We have heard many stories of the Unaka, the white men, who have come to our lands from far off places. They have odd ways of healing their sick…they cut and bleed the ill…the letting of life blood. How strange they are, as many of the ill die from this practice.

As I remember these days of long ago, I'm reminded of the many days spent in sadness over the way the Unaka's diseases spread throughout our villages. Disease, unfortunately, was not the only ailment to hit our People. The men became sickened with the fire water, which made the braves crazy with wild ways. The addiction spread and they cried for more as the warm liquids wrecked their minds and bodies. The blankets and cloth we traded to ward off the cold of the long winters were filled with their diseases. There are some who believed this was done on purpose and there are those whom choose to believe this was not so. Some Unaka were helpful to my people and cared for what happened to us. Many taught us their ways that have helped us much in the moons to follow.

I had no other thoughts of going with Little Owl and the others on a war party until my war skills could be learned and honed to that of the other young braves like my cousins. With time, there were no skills that -with practice- I could not master. My skill with the bow, knife and the muskawano (the white man's gun) would become legendary amongst my people. By age eleven, my skills as a huntress and healer were told in the lodges of many. I was one so young with burdens so large.

My night lost in the woods far from home changed my life forever. Now I would live in pursuit of a peaceful way for my people. That cold night in the dark had opened my young eyes to the light of peace. Without peace, I was sure our people would vanish from this earth. We watched helplessly as our land and game disappeared and sickness came to take our young and old to the spirit world. They leave us with only memories and dreams of them. The Nunnehi was the name of the Spirit people that spoke to me and brought me back home when I was lost in the Smoking Mountains. They came to me and charged me with the care of my people. I would learn well the ways of our leaders, the way of war and peace and the ways to ensure the future of the Cherokee. The time I spent with the Spirit people gave me knowledge that would carry on within me throughout my lifetime that was both a blessing and a curse. My people would have to change our ways of life to have any chance of staying in the homeland of our ancestors. My purpose in this life was to ensure that there remained enough of our people to continue to be a great nation. My uncle Attakullakulla and I were both charged by the Great Spirit to make this so. The people who sought after our lands would not rest until many or all of our people were wiped from the face of the earth. Without peace there would be no chance that we not would vanish from our homeland. We had already seen our way of life disappearing before our eyes; nothing could ever be the same. I understood after those days of being lost that I must learn to see through the wisdom of my uncle's eyes, the ways of peace and war. I would learn all that I could in this life. I would have to be both a peace-keeper and a war woman. Attakullakulla and Oconostoa were great leaders who loved me as much as they loved their own children which allowed me to be raised as the daughter of chiefs: a girl with great purpose.

As the next years of my youth passed by we knew peace amongst the many nations. There were few wars that broke out with other tribes over our boundaries. Trading with the far off Seminole and other southern tribes had gone well. The Western Nations thrived with little to no encroachment from the white settlers. Our numbers also grew to be many through this time. Our towns and villages grew and divided and were in good health. It was as if time stood still and we were happy people.

As I neared the time where the other girls and maidens of my age were preparing to marry I was preparing for the war of the future. Little time I had for games and such, as my learning was not yet done. The Creator was making me into the warrior I would have to be for my People. Young braves would try to catch my eye but no time did I have for their foolish games and teasing. Such feelings would have to wait; the Creator knows what is best and I had not seen yet the warrior he had chosen for me. I had seen myself as belonging only to the Creator and I would wait 'til he sent the right man.

I grew up a child of the water people, the Ani-Yunwiya, the magic people of the Cherokee. Our love of the water was equaled by no other; we understood the power of water, raging water, and that of tranquil water. We admired, respected, and revered all water. It was the giver of life. Water was also the giver of food. The many fish and turtles that filled our pots and lined our hot stones which nourish our bodies and kept us well from the Unaka diseases. Our People began each day anew by bathing to remove the day before, washing away things that make us stink. The daily bathing ritual also warded off unexpected enemies. I have smelled of the many trappers and pioneers as they approached our land. Their stench arrived days before they did, which is partly why they were so easy to track. The white-skinned Unaka were pretty to look at in their finely stitched dressings, but their fancy hides did not mask their scent that traveled many miles ahead of them.

The whites had already begun to take much of our lands, including areas that we hold sacred above much of other land. We now had to avoid places of our sacred ceremonies where we learned rituals from our fathers. It was important that we stayed clear of the unfriendly Unaka. Our lands no longer followed the way of the Ancients where it once teemed with much game, mountain buffalo, elk, goat, and the great bear. Some of these great animal spirits were hunted out by us as well as the Unaka. This means we now must survive on deer, fish and small game to fill our bellies, and keep the nation strong.

Long gone were the days when we would run the mountain buffalo off cliffs to thin their numbers. This practice may seem cruel but it was needed to prevent the destruction of our land and supply of food. We did not let the meat, hides or any part of these great animals be wasted. The old women and children would use the hides to make clothing and shoes; we would dry the meat to be stored for the long days and nights of the coming winter season. Their bones were also used to fashion jewelry and weapons. Some of their great hides were also traded for herbs, salt, and other wares. Our women admired the stones of other places to make special ceremonial clothing and to adorn our bodies.

Few are the memories of the mountain buffalo fore they were but all about hunted away when I was a young child. These once great herds of animals that were plentiful two and one hundred years ago were much desired in the faraway lands across many oceans. It seemed we all had use for these large animals. When others came from across the great oceans they brought with them many weapons we had never seen before. This new weaponry was made from iron. We traded our hides for these weapons and other things that made our lives easier. We came to know that the skins of the mountain buffalo were prized amongst these peoples of lands of far away.

Long ago we established trading routes throughout our American lands. Through the many years of trading, a new language was born, called the trade language. This language has been used since the time of the ancients so that many tribes of the east, west, north and south could speak of their needs and wants with one another.

The Unaka wasted the Creator's trees and the land lay bare in their wake. The way of the People is to flow with the land, not to fight the spirit of nature. Though we cherish the water, we do not put our longhouse close to the river where an unwelcome visitor could wash it away after great anger and rains from the sky. When our people work with the land instead of against it our villages become safer and richer.

We watched the ways of the Unaka and laughed much in the Council House and around our fires. Many of their ways we could not understand as they did not understand many of our ways. We came to know that if we could learn from each other and live in peace it would be the best for all.

Little Owl, Longfellow, me and my many cousins all grew up happy by the Little Tennessee River in the town of Chota. The days were full, filled with many tasks to do before the dark of the moon comes. Our days were spent gathering wood for our cook fires as well as the warming of our longhouses. Cooking and preparing of our meals took much time for the women, children and old ones. All who were able had tasks they must do.

Our longhouses were built from the trees that were too tired to stand toward the sky any longer. It takes many hands to gather these trees as it is hard work. The old people use hatchets to notch out the flesh of the trees where they will be set together. Once they are set together and the roof is in place the longhouse is complete. We take only what is needed from the land the Creator put us upon. We give thanks to all that is used or given.

There was a lot of preparation to enter into the cold season of winter. We had to gather enough wood to heat our lodges. Long days were also spent gathering herbs and leaves for medicines and cooking. There are many kinds of fruits, nuts, vegetables, roots, and berries that had to be collected for the daily meals as well as dried and stored for our winter meals. Passing of time is swift in our village. There are always tasks that need to be completed. The young and old alike dry, cure and cook the meats brought in by the hunting parties. The women make clothes and baskets, and cook pots as well as tend our gardens and fields of crops.

On the day of the passing of my childhood, which comes during the thirteenth year, is when my life forever changed. Standing on the banks of the river that day I spied visitors to our village bathing there before the Council feast. The women of the village had been preparing for days for this ceremonial feast. Tame Deer, my mother, was sure with my childhood antics that I would never come of age to give her the grandchildren she so longed to hold and love and teach the way of the Ancients.

You see, I was always most curious. My mind was never at rest. The running of my mind and tongue has cost me much on countless occasions. It was on this first day of my becoming a woman that I saw this man bathing in the river, the man I instantly wanted to spend the rest of my days with. His chiseled, unclothed body glistened and shimmered in the mid-strike of the rising moon. His black hair shined with the light of the moon and the early stars, and it pierced my soul like an arrow that had been shot straight through to my beating heart.

I moved to catch a better look and as I did I tripped over a fallen branch and landed on the cool, moist earth. The sight of four warriors, now on alert, halted me motionless to the ground. As I had seen my cousin Dragging Canoe do many times before, I began crawling slowly across the ground as we had been taught until I could right myself and run back to the longhouse. If mother spotted me before I could get my soft, white doeskin dress and moccasins clean from my fall, she would bend my ear or worse...not allow me to go on a hunt or join on the war parties.

Along with the other braves and warriors I continued to learn and practice the ways of war as well as that of the Atawehi. My need to know as much about all our ways of life was not shared in the same way of the other girls and women of our clan. There were few war women in our tribe, but I longed to be one of them.

My heart prayed for peace amongst all; my mind and spirit knew this was not to be. The wisdom of the Ancients flowed through my veins and my purpose lay before me. Knowledge would be my power. My eyes had seen what was to come. The Creator had given my eyes the sight of the future and a knowing of the past.

The traditional tasks that were performed by the women - young and old - were important to the clan; I, however, had no interest in such things. I had been taught to do these chores but I felt my knowledge and strengths needed to be utilized learning new things each day, for I knew that the time drew closer that our world would forever be changed and my people would need the knowledge that I carry.

As I hurried from fulfilling yet another task that I lacked desire in, I cleaned the dirt from my dress before the Ritual Ceremony began. Arriving at the ceremony just in time, I felt anguish that the Great Spirit was not shining upon me this day. This night only got worse. My stomach tied in knots at the sight of the young warriors I saw bathing in the river. After all, my crush was one of them... a man I heard my cousin call Kingfisher. He had come to fight in the Creek wars. He was accompanied by other warriors from the Deer Clan.

This night the other maidens and I would dance for the men and warriors of our clan as well as braves and warriors from the other six clans of our tribe. This ceremony marks our passing to the age of marriage. This night many maidens would meet the man that they would join with.

The warriors could not remove their eyes from the many beautiful girls they saw. Ani-Yunwiya are lovely of skin and hair; it is important to our way of life to always be clean. I watched as my cousin Dragging Canoe, who in his youth was known as Little Owl, talked with the friends that he met while he was part of a war party in the lands of Kentucky and Ohio. As Dragging Canoe sat with Kingfisher and they began to talk, I was sure I saw them looking my way. I could no longer see the face of the handsome warrior as he had moved to where his back was facing me. As I caught a smile from my cousin, I was assured Dragging Canoe would speak kindly of me.

I began to dance alongside the other maidens, yet I only had eyes for one warrior. All would surely notice this. Kingfisher held his dark eyes gazing into mine and all else seemed to fade into the distance. As the drums beat out the call from my heart I hoped the man before me would feel the same as I.

I watched this night as many of my maiden friends tried to catch the eye of these warrior men. It is a law that we must join with a warrior of another clan or tribe. The law was meant to keep us separate from our clansmen; we are not to join with a cousin. The way of our law keeps the blood of the People strong and pure. Who would want to join with boys you laughed at and made fun of before they became braves and warriors? It is true our cousins are now swifter than we, but it is hard to erase the thoughts of the boys from our youth. Now that I was a maiden of age to marry, I knew I could not select a husband from the Wolf Clan of my mother or the Bird Clan of my father.

My heart plunged into sadness when I noticed Arabella, my dearest friend, approach Kingfisher. She was surely the most beautiful of our maidens. All the young braves of our village watched her and tried their best to get Arabella to notice them. She would pay them no mind, as our law states. All night I watched her as she tried to catch the eye of the warrior my heart longed for.

For many hours I observed Dragging Canoe laughing by the fire with Kingfisher and other young warriors and braves that were preparing to go on the warpath. They were enjoying a feast before the rites of their fasting began. For three days they would deprive their bodies of food and water to sanctify and purify them. During this time the warriors stayed in a sweat lodge where the Atawehi prepared them for war with our enemy. We would rather be at peace with our red brothers and the Unaka but we did not fear what must be done to protect the Cherokee.

At the end of the three days there was a Scratching Ceremony that marked the end of their fast. This ceremony was also performed by the Atawehi. The scratching of their bodies was done with the claws of a great bear. The flesh of their skin was scratched by these claws as they paid tribute to the Great Spirit. The Chiefs and other honored guests watched this ceremony from the counsel house that is the center of our town. They watched as the warriors went through these purifying rituals to remember the bravest of the men.

Some of the rituals this night, including mine, were led by the Counsel Women and the Chiefs of our tribe who held seats in the Counsel Lodge of Chota. At the end of their ceremonial songs, dances and other tributes to the Great Spirit, our warriors painted their bodies in vermillion red, which is the color of the ground on which we walk and the favored color of our tribe. Since the end of my fifth year I had been attending the council meetings of our Clan. This was a high honor for one so young. My father-uncles had decided my presence would bring me much knowledge of our English father, King George II, as well as the French. Knowledge is power, as they often said.

For five full moons the warriors were gone from Chota. All this time I could only think of one warrior, Kingfisher. Something about this warrior made my blood run warm and my heart beat with the swiftness of a running deer. We speak little of feelings so I knew only what I overheard in the whisperings of the maidens who were newly joined with braves.

Many were the problems that faced my people, but together we did much. The ones whom had seen many moons would sit as sentinels at our crop sites. Our People were often killed or wounded by wild animals, passing strangers, or scouting parties of other tribes who would attempt to steal our crops. The ancient ones were honored to do this job as they were closer to walking with Yawa in the next world. Our grandparents wanted to protect the children - children like me - by guarding our precious crops. The strength of a tribe comes from the foods that we harvest that Mother Earth gives to us.

Not long before my birth my uncles Attakullakulla and Oconostoa came to full power as the Red Chief and White Chief in Chota. They had a village that would be theirs to rule over and to raise their families in. My mother Kati - the one who tames deer- had gone with her brothers, which is how we came to live in Chota. Attakullakulla the Red Chief and my mother were twins and they could not be parted from one another. Mother often said that their hearts beat as one and they feel the joy and pain of the other. Though my mother has many brothers, it is Attakullakulla with whom we feel the closest to.

Chota, our beloved village, sits above the banks of the Little Tennessee River. My family lived along these banks and hills of my childhood. My grandfather, Moytoy, long ago signed a peace treaty and pledged the alliance of our people to King George II, our Father across the sea. My uncles, Attakullakula and Oconstoa, traveled there with four others from our tribe-some of whom were chiefs or would become chiefs of our Nation.

They sailed across the ocean to England on a ship called The Fox with a man called Sir Cummings along with his interpreter guides. There they saw many sights, ate strange foods, and were taken to theaters and were invited to many parties held in their honor. My uncles often told us stories of their long journey to England to see The King and of the many wondrous things they saw there.

Upon The Fox my uncles were on the ocean for three full moons before they reached the King's country. They were gone so long that Attakullakulla returned a man; many months away from home will do that to a boy. Grandfather Moytoy had sent these two sons of his to England to study the ways of the white man; he felt he could only trust his sons to tell him of King George's power and how far reaching his lands were.

The Cherokee visitors were presented to King George II and Queen Caroline of Ansbach while they dined. My Chief Uncles felt a wrong had been done to them when they were not invited to sit and feast with the King and his wife. The interpreter later explained the ways of the white privileged man and my angry uncles eventually had to accept this strange way of showing honor to guests.

My uncles marveled at the splendor in England and learned all that they could. They returned with many gifts of guns, gun powder, and fine cloths from the King and his people. The King said that he loved his children and would protect us from our many enemies. Their journey took more than twelve full moons. Many years later their time in England would prove to hold many keys to the future of our Nation as a people, as a tribe in the land of "America."

Many stories are told from the ancient times of a Spaniard named DeSoto who once came to our land to see what could be of use to his people. There have been many since DeSoto's time that declared our land, like King George, to be theirs by right of discovery. There were also many hunters and trappers that we had to negotiate with that were also trying to take our land from us. Most Unaka were feared by our people, for they laid waste to our land as well as our game.

The settlers from these far off places brought with them their own buffalo (cows) and squealing boar (pigs) with them. The meat of these animals was to be avoided because the flesh of their meat made us sluggish and lazy. The few mountain buffalo that are left, venison, rabbit, squirrel, pheasant and fish nourish our bodies and do not weaken us. The white man had not only invaded our land, but changed our diets. They were beginning to take over and change our ways of life.

As I blossomed into fourteen year old Nanyehi, my mind began to fill with things other than looking for burdock and blackberries. The memory of the warrior, Kingfisher, took front and center. For these many days I prayed to the Great Spirit to return our men safely from the battles with the Creek Nation at the farthest southern parts of our hunting grounds. I also found myself praying that my visions and dreams of Kingfisher living with me in the lodge of my mother were correct.

Soon problems began to arise that overtook my thoughts. The Creek Indians walked our sacred lands to hunt. They were taking more land each season and many Indian Nations began to have the same problems as we. Once, long ago, we believed the Creeks to be our friends and allies, but this was an illusion. They tricked us into a trap and helped our enemies that were trying to defeat us and take our lands.

The Muscogee Indians, known as the Lower Creeks, aligned themselves with the French to take over our lands and set brother against brother. When Chief Moytoy entrusted our lands to the English King it was to protect us from the French invaders. We were quick to learn that the French seldom kept their word. They had planned to set tribe against tribe to wipe us from the face of the Earth. They cared not about the lives of old women and children; we were simply seen as pests that should be destroyed. For many moons my grandfather and uncles spent much time trying to show our Creek brothers as well as many other nations that our best hopes of survival would be to unite as one saving our land and people.

Finally, the day came that Dragging Canoe as well as many other warriors and Chiefs returned from the path of war. The signal was beat out upon the drums to meet at the Council House in the center of Chota. My heart felt like a drained creek, as I saw that Kingfisher was not amongst them. My mind swirled and my body became as hot as an ember from the fires. Was he hurt or - even worse - had he been killed in battle? The last of the warriors trickled into the Council House. My heart sank again for there were still no signs of Kingfisher.

As sadness swelled, my heart began to ache and as hard as I tried to stay seated, I had to escape to the safety of our longhouse. My body, without feeling, slowly approached the longhouse that sat far from the banks of the Little Tennessee River. I was about to enter my home when my name was whispered in a way I had never heard it before... "Nanyehi."

My breath caught in my chest; my heart beat with the swiftness of a pony running wild through the meadows. Kingfisher was alive and standing in front of me! I tried to find my voice but could not speak. Time stood still as I trembled in his stunning presence. We looked into each other's eyes intently; his large, round eyes were dark pools that I found myself lost in.

"Nanyehi," he began again, "We have been gone five full moons. This whole time, I could not remove you from my thoughts. You have captured my heart and a life without you I cannot see. Our destinies are tied together in ways I do not yet understand. All I know is you are to be the mother of my children and only you do I want by my side 'til we are old and the Great Spirit calls us to dwell with him in the sky. Forever will I watch over you my beloved. Tell me... does your heart feel the same as mine?"

Still, I struggled to find my voice. The stirring of my heart was like that of a great storm. My limbs were numb, my heart swelled and felt as though it would burst. These were the words I had longed to hear but dared not hope for. This beautiful warrior was to be mine, and I his. Our hearts were singing the same song.

We continued to gaze deeply into the each other's eyes and without the need of words, I knew he would be mine forever. When I at last find my voice, it was that of a woman, no longer a timid girl nervous in the presence of a great man.

"Kingfisher, my days, nights, and dreams have been full with only you. From the moment I saw you, I've thought of no other. The Spirit has been whispering in my ear that you are the one."

Then Kingfisher reached out to me and stroked the skin of my cheek, saying, "You are beautiful. Your skin is as soft and blushed as your childhood name, Wild Rose."

It was the first time he touched me and it tingled where his hand had brushed against my cheek. My heart soared like an eagle. Kingfisher slowly opened his arms and I walked into them. Never could I remember feeling as safe as I did when wrapped in the strong arms of my warrior. We stood like this for a time then he said, "I will come to you at the strike of the next full moon and we will make our marriage plans where I will join your family. I will go to my village to gather my belongings then I will return to Chota with my family, bearing gifts and to ask of your uncles that we be married." Again, he held my face and looked into my eyes and I trembled. Not with fear but with the fire of my blood that now ran as hot as the embers from the Eternal Flame.

The many nights ahead would be long and lonely. My thoughts filled with the family Kingfisher and I would one day have. I dreamed of him working at my side to build a stronger nation for our people. My future husband would surely do great things for the Wolf Clan. He would return and become one of our most honored warriors.

True to his word, when the next full moon appeared outside our longhouse, so did Kingfisher. Our embrace was long and hard as we spoke the words of love we longed to say to one another. By way of tradition it was custom that the man ask of our fathers the right to marry. Being that my father was killed when I was but a seed in my mother's womb, Kingfisher would have to ask my uncles for their blessing that was needed for our union.

Kingfisher then came to me and announced, "I have spoken to Attakullakulla and Oconostoa and have asked for their blessing of our union. They are in agreement and are pleased that we should join in the marriage ceremony this day." Once again Kingfisher opened his arms to me and I walked into his safety. He lifted me from my feet into his warm, strong embrace. We spun around and around and shouted of our happiness; then we laughed as small children.

Mother came from the longhouse and wanted to know what all the giggling was about. After I told her of our news she began gathering the things that would be needed later that day for the marriage ceremony.

Kingfisher's family made themselves a camp by our lodge and began settling in for the festivities. It is not uncommon for a marriage to be planned with little notice as our ceremonies are traditionally simple. Mother prepared for our ceremony along with Kingfisher's mother. They were already becoming family. Both were smiling as they worked alongside each other.

I spoke to Kingfisher, saying, "Dragging Canoe has spoken often of you by the council fire. He speaks highly of the other warriors and you. He told the Council of your great warrior ways and of the things he has learned from your skills.

Even as we speak, our young braves are learning from your clan's ways of battle. Kingfisher, I know you are led, as am I, by the Great Spirit toward peace. We must both be true to our spirit guides and honor our people."

Kingfisher told me of what Dragging Canoe said. His words touched my spirit. Kingfisher began saying, "On the many trails we took, your cousin spoke highly of you." He paused. "Dragging Canoe feels you are being led to work for peace among all people, including Unaka as well as the other Indian Nations."

41

Then Kingfisher spoke more softly, "You are the most revered woman in the Cherokee nation, your wisdom is matched by no other, your beauty is to behold and your heart is softer than a fawn's coat. Nanyehi, I have loved you since the night I saw you watching us bathe in the river before the ritual feast. I knew I would love you forever when I saw the pain that etched across your face for me during the Scratching Ceremony. I have loved you since the beginning of my time for all has led me to your lodge. Our destinies are tied together. I also long for peace among all of our red and white brothers. Your cry is my cry: that of peace. Our paths have joined together that I may aid you in the journey you are destined for in this life. I will love no other than you all my days."

I felt the sting of tears in my eyes as he spoke these words of bravery and love to me. As sure as the words he spoke to me, I knew I would feel no love stronger than this for all time.

Kingfisher's mother, Mariah, as well as his brother, 'Taw you ne' see', had traveled to Chota to take part in our marriage ceremony. As was meant to be, Kingfisher and I would say our vows on this day.

Two priests walked into the Counsel House, one each escorting Kingfisher and I to the center. The priests then parted to stand toward the east and we faced the west. Mariah stood proudly at Kingfisher's side holding her gifts of venison and fur. Kati and I stood together, holding the gifts of corn and blankets. She also held a belt of vermillion and black that I made for Kingfisher out of blinding love through the many moons he was gone from me. Longfellow, my brother, stood at our mother's side. This signified his willingness to be responsible for me and my children. We entered the counsel house draped in blankets of blue which represents our old lives. The priest prayed a blessing over us that we may have long lives together and be happy.

42

Kingfisher then accepted the belt that I had fashioned those many weeks and placed it around his waist. Our mothers gave us the gifts they carried and Kingfisher and I exchanged these gifts between each other. We then placed our blue blankets together as one. The two-sided wedding vase was then drunk from east to west and north to south, thus giving blessings to all the directions. We both threw it to the ground and watched it shatter to signify we are now united as one in this life. Then a white blanket was placed around our shoulders and we left the Counsel House united as one.

We left the Counsel House and started towards my mother's longhouse. As we walked slowly through Chota we were greeted by my many aunts, uncles, and cousins. My family was very happy for us. They saw, as I did, that the Creator had chosen well for me.

When we arrived home, Kingfisher took me aside and asked if I would accompany him on a journey to a place he wanted to share with me alone. I quickly agreed and we prepared to depart. I was excited to embark on our first adventure together as one.

Thus, Kingfisher and I began our journey, traveling to a special place he had chosen for our first coupling. We went far to the south and east; we rode through the night and most of the next day without stopping to sleep before we reached the destination.

The last mile of our journey, there began a rumbling and I wondered where my new husband was taking me. My anticipation of our coupling was so strong I wished much that Kingfisher had chosen to stay in my beloved Chota for I longed to lay by his side. For many miles I wondered what far off place we could be traveling to. I had no fear for I trusted Kingfisher, and trusted above all that the Great Spirit would not let us be lead into any danger. I had never traveled such a distance from Chota before without the presence of my mother.

Always my people had trusted and sought out my council as I had been touched by the Great Spirit. Many times each day my chores were interrupted by the people seeking advice from me. I knew that as Nanyehi my life was not my own; but as hard as it was many days I knew that to be in service of the Great Spirit was an honor and not to be questioned.

Now my faith was blind and I could not see what was to be. The Spirit has talked to me from the time I was but a young girl, but he was not talking to me now. All I could hear was the thunder of water and see the smoke from the fires of the Nunnehi, The Little People, who dwell beneath the mountains. Today these people were busy with many fires for the smoke around the mountains was thick with the talking of the smoke of time, our time.

As we approached the river, we could hear the thunder of the falling waters and a mist arose from the area near where the water fell to the rocks. Kingfisher bade me to dismount my pony. After he had hobbled our ponies, my husband gently took my hand in his as we walked toward the rocks around these great falling waters, such a place of wondrous beauty to behold! It is here we would couple. Kingfisher signaled for me to follow him. We walked up a sloping face of stone and passed over large stones in the pool at the base of the falls. We passed through a place behind the great falling waters and there his chosen place came into view. Kingfisher once again took my hand and brought me to his embrace. Such peace and safety I had never known. My body shook. "Are you afraid?" Kingfisher asked.

"No, not as long as you are by my side." Here in this place Kingfisher and I were to become as one; I trembled in anticipation. Kingfisher had taken great care to plan this time for us. In the cave behind the falling waters were many beautiful earthen pots that held inside a store of food and beautiful skins of fur.

Kingfisher took a large, long-haired buffalo skin and spread it before us. He told me this white buffalo skin was long ago hunted from our land. We still have many skins of the mighty mountain buffalo but this was the skin of the great white buffalo, of which I was amazed at its color and size. Many nights I listened to our Ancient ones tell of these revered animals that once freely roamed our land. With the white buffalo gone from our lands we knew the Creator would be displeased. Part of our punishment we had already seen happen among our People. There were some of the ancients that felt we would pay with many losses for not keeping the land safe as the Creator had commanded of his people. This creature held much power; some of the people even believed it was magical. We were allowed to hunt his brown brother but not its white brother. If you found a white buffalo that had lain down to die, then he had given you his spirit as a gift. As is our way, nothing was to be wasted that the animal spirit chose to give us. We still use the many tools and sacred ceremonial gifts that were made from the spirit of these great animals.

After Kingfisher had prepared our sleeping mat, he came to me and took my face in his powerful hands and gently placed his lips upon mine. My mind swirled at the thought of this man and this magical place. Kingfisher then said, "You are my destiny and I yours. Long are the days I have waited for you to become a woman."

I replied, "I too have waited for this moment in our time; for the Great Spirit has long shown me of your coming. Yours is the face I have seen in my dreams and visions."

Then Kingfisher lifted me into his arms and gently laid me upon the longhaired fur that enveloped my body. It set my skin on fire. Slowly Kingfisher began to undo the tethers of my dress and laid it open. It seemed as though his eyes forever roamed my body.

"You are beautiful," he said and laid his hands upon my skin where he traced with his fingers the swelling mounds of my breasts. He then laid his hand against my heart that was beating wildly, so wildly that I was waiting for it to burst from my chest.

We laid side by side for what seemed to be hours tracing the curves and lines of each other's bodies, forever etching these memories into the maps of our minds. We rocked and moaned with a pleasure I had never known existed. This lovemaking was almost more than I could bear, for Kingfisher still had not entered the sacred area where my soul awaited.

Kingfisher once again took my face in his hands and said, "Are you ready my beloved?" I could not find my voice, it escaped me, and I nodded my approval and watched as his eyes became as dark pools of dancing light. Gently he stroked me and my hips pulsated to the beat of our own music. I stroked him to the same beat I heard in my head. As our bodies become one, we began with the beat of a slow gentle rocking, then to a quick, burning rhythm as our souls exploded into one.

The streaming light that pierced through the falls cast a golden light that bathed all around us. Exhausted, we fell into each other's arms and into a deep sleep, a sleep of peace and joy. Playing in the meadows of our dreams, the fast falling waters roared around us.

When we awoke, it was on the second day after our marriage ceremony in Chota. Never had I been away from my home this many sunsets without my mother. Time seemed to be standing still. I thanked the Creator as I knew such a time of love and playfulness would likely never be ours again.

This day the Dream Spirit showed me the light of my firstborn's eyes. For on the first time we shared love came the seed of our daughter.

Kingfisher spoke to me, "Nanyehi, the reason I brought you here was to take you far away from the demands of the people. I would never ask that you turn your back on them, but for this moment in time, I wanted you to myself. Come. Arise. We go to another place."

I did not want to leave this place of love. As he began gathering our belongings, I started to bath in the back splash of the falls. The water was cool and refreshing. My body shivered in the chill of the water, then felt warmth coming from his body as he nestled close to mine. I felt the power of his manhood as he held me closely. Our bodies fit together as tightly as the feathers of the eagle's wings. We came together as one again in this beautiful place with the water falling and roaring down around us.

So it was; we packed our ponies and started away from the falls, such a wondrous place of beauty rivaled by no other. As we traveled downstream and when we were far enough from the loudness of the falls that I could hear the breathing sounds of my husband. I asked of him, "Kingfisher, what is this place?"

"We are near a trading route that has been used since the time of the Ancients. Look well my love mark in your mind the ways of the river, the places where the creeks and small falling waters enter her banks," he told me. Kingfisher and I stopped and then began to unpack our belongings. Then he set our ponies free.

Kingfisher took our belongings and started to cross the river at a low spot. There were large rocks that we could walk upon to cross the river. I followed his lead, stepped only where he stepped, stopping only when he stopped. I was tracing the path that we took over and over in my mind. Not wanting to forget any mark that showed me where we were going.

We stopped at a small waterfall that flowed into the river where there below it came to a place that slowed and widened out. It was here we began to climb the side of the mountain. I looked across the river where we had just crossed and studied the stone cliff. There in the rock face was the form of a striking snake that seemed to be guarding the river as a sentinel. We followed the deer and elk path up the side of the mountain.

Everywhere I looked there were flowering bushes that laid heavy with buds. All over the side of this mountain were azalea, laurel bushes and rhododendron. We stopped by a large boulder and walked around to its backside and there came into view a small path that was well hidden. We walked low along this path till we came upon a small dwelling that was nestled into the mountain cliff covered on all sides by bushes that would flower beautifully come spring. After the cold of winter this glorious place would be alive with colors of pinks, reds and white. The bushes all mixed together made a wondrously beautiful blanket under the large open canopy of trees upon the mountainsides.

Kingfisher set our belongings inside the dwelling and silently took my hand in his and we began walking slowly towards the top of the mountain. As we neared the top of the mountain we stopped and he asked of me, "Look all around you my beloved, and tell me what you see."

"Kingfisher, my eyes are filled with only you and that is all I wish to see. Come to me my husband that I may see you even more." We kissed and made each other feel the heat rise from within. There under the blue skies, we made love again.

"Have you seen enough?" he asked playfully. "Nanyehi, my wife, look around you and tell me of what you see."

As I began to look around me and trace a map of this place into my minds' eye, a small falling creek was to my left, a flowing river was below, and to my surprise there was a face of an ancient one that appeared to be carved into the stone face of the cliff on the other side of the river. "Husband, this place is truly special. I see we are being watched over by an Ancient One. "We are to stay here?" I asked of him. He was slow to answer; I could tell he was deep in his mind. I reached up and touched his brow and wiped a single tear that etched his cheek.

He answered, "This will always be our special place, a place to rest, to play and to love one another. If ever we are separated come and wait for me here, for this is a place of safety. This I built for you that you would always have a place to come and rest if the demands of our people become too much for you to bear, my beloved." He paused, "Come, follow me."

We walked back through the maze of rhododendron so tall that there was no space to walk underneath. In this maze he had built a small house of large tree branches and carefully placed stones. He had built for us a special nest high above the river, hidden there, amongst stone and flowers. A place our love could grow freely.

As the days passed sweetly I grew to know and sense Kingfisher's every need and he mine. I could sense when he was hungry for food or hungry for me by the look in his eyes or the smile that graced his face. We grew close, so close I felt our love could keep us alive forever. I also grew to sense when he needed to be by himself. We never spoke of leaving this magical place nestled in the side of our mountain.

So happy was I that Kingfisher had brought us to this place far from the village I so loved. With the problems of the people so great it left me feeling drained much of the time. Each day brings to me the woes of Chota, of family and those whom sought refuge among us. The French were becoming more forceful with their demands. The pale skinned Unaka were approaching from every direction. But here in this magical place my only thoughts were of my husband and family to be.

We spent the next two full moons this way: bathing in the river each morning, gathering berries, nuts, fruits and seeds. We would hunt small game together for our cook pot and eat lazily, watching as the hawk and eagle flew their hunting grounds searching for prey and watching the lazy flow of the river wrapped in each other's arms. How sweet this time was. I knew that his love for me grew with each passing moon, and felt the tenderness of his movements.

Off to the north we could see where the mist arose from the place of the great falling waters, our first place of love. It was there that we would often venture to bathe and bask in our love in the pool at the base of the falls.

We did not speak of leaving but knew the time was coming where we would have to venture from this place of wonder and beauty. This spot has long been used in ceremonies of many kinds. Soon there would be others who would travel to this place and it would no longer be ours.

The third full moon was when the sickness began. Kingfisher said, "I am sure that there is a child growing within." He placed his hand on the small bump of my stomach that was now noticeable. Each day I had silently prayed for our child to be strong and healthy. Now, as one, we prayed to the Creator.

Kingfisher began, "Father Creator hear my prayer. Watch over Nanyehi and our wee one, keep them safe from harm. We are here to serve you and keep watch upon your lands. Teach me to love my family as you love us. Help me protect my beloved, keep me strong."

I continued, "My Creator, bless my husband and the child that I carry. Keep them and me away from harm. Protect us from our enemies and may we be invisible on our journey home. You have shown me your plan for my life. Keep my mind wise and sharp as the owls. Let us always be thankful and kind to each other. Let us above all serve you and keep the promise of our Ancestors."

We journeyed back to Chota much slower than we had left for the mountain water falls, our special place where we made our first child.

Mother spotted us from the stream where she gathered water and ran all the way to the longhouse to greet us. We flew into each other's embrace, for never had I been separated so long from her. Three full moons seemed like a lifetime. I left her a young girl and returned a woman who would now also become a mother.

We chatted like two squirrels for a time while Kingfisher unpacked our supplies. As is our custom, while we were away the village worked together to enlarge our home. For Kingfisher was now to dwell with my family in the lodge of my mother that would one day be mine, as was the law. All property belongs to the woman and is passed forward to her granddaughters. Kingfisher was now of the Wolf Clan and left behind the Deer Clan of his mother.

Amongst the Cherokee, there are seven clans, seven being the perfect number of the Creator. Seven days, seven clans, seven points to the star. The clans are: The Wolf Clan, The Deer Clan, Bird Clan, Plant Clan, Wild Potato Clan, Longhaired Clan and the Blue Clan. My people, the Wolf Clan, are the most revered and honored of the seven clans of the original people.

We are the special tribe, known amongst all Nations as the Magic People of the original clans of the Cherokee.

The drums of the Counsel House beat out the signal for us to gather. Our Counsel House was the largest in the tribe. Chota is the capital of our Nation. It is here that most of the meetings of the seven clans are held. In times of celebration or threat of war this is where we met. Many of our clan and others gathered here to listen as our chiefs and leaders spoke.

Chief Attakullakulla, by custom, would speak first to all the people. His skill as negotiator with the King's men, as well as with the Unaka, was sought out by many. His small stature, kind face, and quick wit brought him much respect. The Great Peace Chief was wise and his words rang in the ears of those who sought his council. He spoke out to the People that were gathered at the Council House. "The Creeks are hunting within our borders once more. They are at war with all that crossed their path except for the French. The Creeks do not want peace with anyone."

"I have sent many Peace Chiefs to reason with the Creek Chiefs to try and stop this coming war. Oconostoa sent Dragging Canoe with many other war chiefs and warriors; they have gone to the south to push the Creeks back toward their own villages. They come to hunt our grounds instead of their own. We will have less game to hunt come winter because of this. We must work toward peace with our brothers to the south, but so far they resist. We have long talked with our Muskogee brothers, for in the smoke of time we will surely need to ally. The French soldiers are staying in their towns and villages; they have swayed them to fight against the English. Together we could work as one to protect our lands from all whites. My People, I work to keep peace with all men as the Creator wishes us to do. Not always do we survive, but win victories we must. They will never leave our lands.

All nations together must unite against the Unaka, who are taking our land for little or nothing. We must not trade for such things as trinkets and whiskey any longer. These things do not last and bring us no benefit. The land lives on forever; we are the true keepers of this land provided by the Creator." He ended and returned to his seat in the center of the Council House.

Chief Oconostota rose to speak. He stood straight and proud and then turned in all directions to look into the faces of those in the circle. The Great War Chief addressed his people. He spoke loudly, "This day the Creek has killed an entire white family. The Unaka will not care that our people had nothing to do with this senseless killing of these men along with their women and children. This killing goes against the beliefs of the Ani Yunwiya, but not all of our cousins believe the same as we.

Chief Attakullakulla has spoken true, we must be prepared. For the soldiers will not care that we had nothing to do with these senseless deaths. They will strike and take many lives for the lives of the lost white settlers. Chief Attakullakulla prepares for the journey to Charles Town to talk with the King's men in hopes they will be able to protect us from what is to come." Slowly he again began to turn and face all there and began again to speak.

"Now many of our young warrior chiefs and braves move to our land to the south to protect our borders against the Creek. Kingfisher, you have just returned, but we have need of you in this war. Will you lead other brave warriors of the Wolf Clan?" Oconostoa asked.

Kingfisher nodded his agreement. Oconostoa continued, "Kingfisher is a trusted War Chief of the Deer Clan who married my daughter-niece and we have many hopes set upon him. The skills of Kingfisher are many. He is wise of mind and well-trained in the way of war to lead the Cherokee. His heart believes as mine, that peace is truly the way of survival for the People, but as War Chief all that can matter is survival."

Chief Oconostota spoke firmly, "Go my people and ready yourselves. We must not be surprised. Make ready for what may come. Now go and prepare your families."

The People left the Counsel House quietly, deep in thought of what all must be done. Kingfisher and I walked together toward our home.

How long ago it already seemed that we had gone to our special place. I was now three full moons with child. How proud I felt to be his woman! He was beautiful inside and out. My heart ached at the thought of being away from him for even a moon, let alone the length of a war. For how long he would be gone, I did not know.

The Great Spirit often sent me visions but they were seldom about me. This gift often felt more a curse, for knowing what is to be before it happens sometimes I cannot find the use in the knowing. How am I to tell someone that their loved one now walks in the sky with the Creator and with those who have passed on before?

The Ancient Ones told the story of the Ani'-Kuta'ni, the mound builders and priests of the Cherokee. They committed crimes against our own people and set fear into them. They used their gifts of knowing to control the People and commit their will upon them. This blood line was put to death by the Kittawa Society long after one of the Priests used his power to take from a chief his very own wife.

Our People have strong desires to know the future and there are those of us whom have the answers to what people wish to know. When someone becomes sick, I know by touching them or even talking to them if they will recover or not. This I sometimes keep to myself or tell them soon all will be well. For is the knowing and fearing worth the space in their head? All is well if soon they will rest in the arms of the Great Shepherd. If they will recover and be well again, I tell them so.

The hardest to know and understand were the Seekers. These were the ones who walked past death and seemed lost in our world. These Spirit People may come to me anywhere, even to the door of my lodge, though they do not enter, but wait outside for me to help them or send them to place of the Creator. I tell you these things, that you may better understand me.

Kati and I prepared Kingfisher for his journey. He would leave before the rise of the morning sun with his warriors to join with Dragging Canoe in the fight against the Creeks to drive them from our lands. After all the preparations had been made, Kingfisher and I retired to our part of the longhouse. I took Kingfishers hand and held it close to my heart and prayed for the Great Spirit to watch over my husband and to return him safely to us. My prayer to the Creator was this:

"Creator, hear me. We come on our knees before you. We await your guidance to show us the best way to help our family and to do what is best for all people. Let not these honors bestowed upon us lead our head but keep you the center of all we do. Yawa, these days are full of danger for all people. The only one we trust is You. May your spirit guide us through these days of war and danger. Together our hearts cry for a peace we fear will never come."

Kingfisher looked into my eyes and said, "Nanyehi, my love for you grows stronger every day, and for our child which grows inside of you. I will return well before the birth of our little one. You both be well." Kingfisher paused and pulled me close to him "I know your mother will be by your side. Let not the demands of the People wear you down, you need all your strength to give our child all it needs. Now come to me skinny woman that I may know you through this night and be of my oneness," he said passionately.

When the morning arrived, we awoke and bathed together for what may be the last in many long moons. His journey south would be a long one and full of danger for him and the other warriors.

I went again into his arms saying, "My husband, I honor you; you will be a great chief of the Wolf Clan. As a child, and even now, the White Wolf has appeared at most of the important events of my life. I was given this gift by Oconostota on my tenth year after my night in the forest when I became known as Nanyehi." I opened my pouch and removed an amulet and presented it to Kingfisher. "Wear this amulet of the White Wolf. It will guard and protect you while you are far from me." I spoke hoping that I sounded braver than I felt inside.

I placed my most treasured possession, a carved white wolf head, around his neck and positioned it over his heart. "My heart goes with you my husband. I will grow fat with child by the fire while you are gone, so maybe I will not mind so much that you are not here, to see me as such." I teased as I ran my hands over the pooch of my stomach.

"You, my beloved, could never be fat. I will miss you, skinny woman," he whispered. With that, he swung up on his pony and rode away, taking my heart with him.

Our ponies were not often used in war as they were not able to move swiftly and quietly through the dangerous mountainous areas. Today they would use these ponies to ride toward a lower river so they could gain time as Dragging Canoe had left two days before.

Time had gone so swiftly after our coupling. I was gone from Chota for three full moons and in that time my people had stored up their many problems and questions. It seemed that I would answer one problem, then another would show up at our longhouse.

The next three full moons seemed to draw by slowly, all the chores that once brought me such joy in days past seems to bring me no happiness at all. The child I was carrying would not allow for travel to the other villages and towns around Chota. My days were long, the nights even longer, and my tiredness frightened me. My hands and feet were swollen and tender most of every day. Every night as I lay down on my lonely bed mat, my mother Kati would put cool, wet skins on my legs and soak my hands in bowls of cold water from the spring. We would add herbs to aid in the relief of the swelling. She would not let me out of her sight for any reason now.

I was full with child when a runner from the war party came to Chota to inform the Chiefs of their progress in the war against the Muscogee Creeks. The Counsel drums were beaten. I readied myself for the walk towards the Counsel House.

My heart was beating swiftly as we approached the Counsel House. When I walked in the seats were almost full. The faces were filled with a mix of fear and hopefulness. As the runner began to speak of their many battles, my heart enlarged with pride; my husband was authoring many stories that will be told by fires for all time. Dragging Canoe and Kingfisher showed much skill and bravery through these battles. His training these many years now served our people well. His foresight and bravery were to be admired by all. As the runner finished with his message, the Chiefs became restless.

Chief Oconostota stood to speak. "People, the days I have long feared are upon us. The Creeks have gathered other tribes against us. They wish to take our hunting grounds from us and this cannot happen. Our numbers are many and we must protect ourselves from the invaders of our lands. We must assure the English of our allegiance with our white brothers. There are many who truly see us as savages not worthy of the lands we live upon. Chief Attakullakulla has always worked for peace with our white brothers. He is wise and has always worked for the good of our people. Even now he is in Charles Town, talking with the King's men and negotiating to keep Chota and our Nation safe. There will come a time, I fear, he will not be able to convince them of our desire to live in peace with all. To the North, the Unaka; to the East, our English brothers; to the South, the French and our enemy the Creek; to the West, there are even more enemies." Oconostota paused. "I will send word to Attakullakulla at Charles Town as he must be advised of these many things that have happened."

"We have much to be proud of. Our warriors are holding our boundaries. The Creek dogs must be pushed back. We must unite our tribe and its many clans to keep the Creeks inside their own borders. Negotiating with their Chiefs is of no use as they have no control over their warriors. The French have armed the Creek and Shawnee with mussawacon [muskets] and their iron swords and they bribe them with trinkets. Their Chiefs have grown old and tired and the young warriors are hungry for power, our blood and our land," he stated boldly.

"People, go and prepare. Help ready the next group of brave warriors that we send to continue the battle against our enemies. We will also send messages to the other Clans of the Cherokee Nation. Together we must decide the fate of our land."

Oconostota looked at me as well as the other elders and Chiefs. We knew this look well and all the leaders stayed behind while the others left the Counsel House. Once it had emptied and we were alone he began speaking on how best to go forward with what must be done.

My uncle spoke to the elders and leaders of our clan. With his wisdom we decided to send each leader where they felt they could do best at convincing the Chief of the towns and villages and other clan leaders of the necessity for all to meet. We all felt it was best that together we make the decisions that needed to be made as a Nation united.

In times of peace we seldom met except for large ceremonies or celebrations. Clan leaders are chosen by the wisdom of our elders. My grandfather Moytoy was the second Principal Chief of our Nation. Before that time there had not been only one leader but many led together. My uncles held this honor in Chota together. Their youngest brother Ammouskossittee became the Chief of Great Tellico. The English elevated him to Emperor after my grandfather Moytoy was killed in battle. Ammouskossittee was but thirteen when grandfather died.

The English right of inheritance elevated him to his father's position. The King felt Ammouskossittee being so young could be controlled whereas my grandfather had been considered a risk to the Crown.

After the death of Moytoy, Chota was made the capital of our Nation. All three brothers: Attakullakulla, Oconostoa, and Ammouskossittee worked together to appease the English. The brothers felt Ammouskossittee was not yet ready to lead his People, so they taught him as best they could.

I so longed to see Kingfisher with my own eyes. I would best serve the people by staying where I could advise and help ready the new group of warriors that would soon join the war party.   A sudden feeling of dread came upon me and I felt mother and I should return home swiftly.   Surely when we arrived all would be revealed, but my feet could not take me there swiftly enough.

When Cherokee women put their minds and hands to task, all will be done the right way. Kati took my hand and guided me toward our home. As we made our way back to the longhouse, we stopped to rest many times at different relatives' homes. This walk seemed to take longer than it should. With each step the longing to get to our longhouse became more urgent.

As I looked into the eyes of my people I could see their strength building with each passing moment. We would band together as our ancestors did before us, the way we always have. The smoke of the past goes with our men and the stories are told by our fires in the night and from them we still learn today. My children will one day share these same stories of our past and the present.

We arrived to a flurry of activity back at the longhouse. Longfellow, my brother, the strong and mighty war chief, had returned from the South. He was wounded and needed healing, which he only trusted his mother and sister to do. Longfellow was now known amongst the people and the whites as The Raven of Chota. But to mother and I he was still Longfellow, as I was to him still Wild Rose.

The Atawehi had already been sent for but our mother had quickly set about cleaning Longfellow's wounds. Meanwhile, I began to gather and prepare the proper herbs for a poultice. We had to act quickly to begin the healing; waiting for the medicine man to arrive would only prolong the infection. His wounds were deep and needed much care. Mother carefully cleaned the worst of his gashes first. We worked through the night cleaning and tending to my brother's injuries.   It had taken him many moons to return to Chota after he had received these wounds and they were fire red and swollen with infection.

After the dawn of the next morning the medicine man made his way to our part of the village. The Atawehi checked the poultices and bandages. He gave his approval of the herbs that were used to tend his wounds. He knew that he need not come to our lodge for Longfellow would already have had the best of care from the healers in his family. Longfellow was very tired and had need of much rest. After all his wounds had been tended to, he was fed broth from the cook pot that had been filled with healing herbs.

In our homes we were always mindful to have food ready to be eaten at all times. One never knows when a stranger or a friend may stop at our lodge. Custom is that we offer food to all whom we welcome. Hence, there is always stew or soup and bread next to the cook fire.

The next day I spent resting. I was again swollen to twice my size and needed to sleep. As tired as she was, Mother stayed awake to look after both of her children whom needed tending.

Longfellow awoke on the second morning feeling much better after his sleep and the healing broth mother had lovingly and gently fed him. He told us many stories from the war with the Creek. Our warriors, though fewer, were the better planners and fighters. Our war ways had helped our people retain our hunting grounds. Such pride I felt knowing that my husband was one of the leading War Chiefs in this battle.

My sleep was fitful all throughout the night. Dreams filled with many faces that I did not know confused me. The dreams that are sent to me do not always make sense when they come. Sometimes it takes many moons or years before I am able to fully piece together their meaning. This dream was full of many faces of Unaka, half-bloods who have the faces of the two peoples mixed together. The Creator sends me these dream visions often, though there is nothing I can do to change what is to be.

Sometimes a knowing or a sense of threat will come over me and I am able to warn a friend or a loved one to take special care as they might be headed into danger. I remain grateful to the Creator for He has given me these gifts. These gifts have changed throughout the years, but are gifts from the Creator all the same. However, there are many nights that I lay awake and wonder if these gifts are worth the hurt that they can cause. Sometimes spirits will come to me. I do not understand why they seek me out; I only know that they do. I do not use my knowledge for gain or profit of any sort; my gifts are used only to help others.

On this night, the vision dream was very different. I saw many longhouses made of stone and things I had never seen before. Some of these longhouses were very tall and when the sun hit them, they shone and reflected the rays of the sun. There were many people with skins of all colors in a land and place I did not know.

I do not see myself as special, although my people do. Many times they come to me with a mystery or dream they do not understand and seek my knowing. Sometimes I will see the answers to what they ask and at times I just know the answers to their questions before it has been asked.

When the spirits of those that have gone to the next world come to me, sometimes it is to send a message to a loved one. Some spirits ask the way home to the Creator, and this is the most special of all the gifts. Some of those that have crossed to the other world appear only to say farewell.

I recall a time when I was young, the Unaka's sickness came to our village and the Great Spirit directed us to leave. We went far away into the thickly wooded forest of the mountains so that we would not get the sickness. My grandfather, Chief Moytoy, took our family and others of our clan that were not already ill and traveled deep into the Smoking Mountains. Moytoy's position as a principal chief made his safety and ours of great importance to the Cherokee Nation.

Little Owl and Oconostoa were left behind as they had been stricken with the illness that we were trying to escape. Both came down with the sickness that moved swiftly through our towns and villages. They were both left with scars that followed them for the rest of their lives. The English called this sickness small pox. Oconostoa's English wife caught this illness which took her life from this earth and her adopted people.

This sickness took half our numbers from us. Many villages and towns were wiped from the face of the land. Some tribes lost even more than we did and forever vanished from the earth. There were many who took their own lives after seeing the skin they were left with. We are a vain people who have taken pride in ourselves and how we appear.

My Grandfather's sons and daughters and their children had to be protected so that our clan's knowledge and wisdom would not be wiped from the land. The blood of ancient warriors, healers, and chiefs flows within our blood. We were trusted to hold sacred the ancient stories for the future of our People.

During our time in the mountains, far away from Chota, the spirits of our dead family came and spoke to me there. I know there are others who see what I see, for they too have been chosen by the Great Spirit. For on this night, the one who came to me was my white mother, Aunt Lucy. My mother asked why I was so sad and I told her of my dream. She had come to me there, beautifully bathed in all white, and she shined with bright, pure love. She called me her daughter and wished love and peace for my life. She told me to be brave and strong that my life would have more meaning than I could understand and that I would know great love in this lifetime.

The following day I recalled this visit to my mother Kati. She looked at me with tears in her eyes and began to tell me this story, one she would repeat from then forward, many, many times.

On the same cold night I had been born, Oconostoa's wife Lucy also gave birth to a girl child. The night in my Uncle's winter lodge had been much different from the lodge of my Mother's.

Su Gi went to her son's lodge in the early morning light to share the news of my birth with Lucy. When Su Gi arrived it was to the sadness of her children. Lucy's child had been born blue for the life cord had wrapped around her neck. The Atiwehi had tried to breathe life back into the wee one but she never awoke from the sleep she had fallen into. Su Gi did all that she could to comfort the distraught Lucy before she returned to my mother's lodge.

In the days that followed my birth, Kati saw that all was not well with her mother. She had asked many times why she was so sad. Su Gi not wanting to upset my mother told her nothing. After many days of rest, Su Gi finally told my mother of Lucy and Oconostoa's loss. The Grandmother was fearful for Lucy as she still was weak from the birth of her child and her grief was great. My Uncle tried his best to comfort her but still all she could do was cry throughout the days and nights. She grew weaker with each passing hour.

When my Uncle came to our lodge to speak with Su Gi, he saw the sadness across his sister's face and knew she understood his loss. They talked for a time and it was decided that he would bring his wife to our lodge so that she could be cared for by my Grandmother.

After two moons of full grieving, Lucy had grown very weak from crying and refusing all food and water. If this continued, she would not live long. My mother was not going to allow her close friend to pass from this life without trying to help her in every way possible. The love my mother had for her brother's wife was deep and true.

As sadness looked to swallow Lucy alive, my mother, with me in her arms, went and rested upon the same mat as my Aunt. She placed me upon my Aunt and in the bravest voice she could speak, she offered me to my Aunt to raise me as her own. This was done from a place of pure love. Though it was breaking my mother's heart to do so, she placed me in the arms of my Aunt. Lucy did not speak, but gently accepted me into her arms. Mother did not show her sadness but arose from the mat and went to the fire and began to prepare a meal for all. My brother, Longfellow had been returned to our longhouse from Attakullakulla's lodge. Being a young boy, full of life, Kati realized she would have many trials to raise an active son like this one. Her heart was breaking but she felt she had done the right thing. The day passed to night and Kati went about preparing what was needed to lay Longfellow down for the night. Lucy took care of me throughout the day and night. When the morning came, Lucy began preparing to return back to her longhouse.

Oconostoa arrived before the sun broke over the mountains. This season was colder than anyone could remember and he came with another coat for his wife. He embraced my mother and thanked her for her loving gestures to him and Lucy. My Aunt placed me in her husband's arms and prepared to depart. When she had readied herself to leave, my Uncle placed her back in my Aunt's arms. My mother held back her tears, there was a piece of her dying inside her heart. Knowing her brother and sister would love and care for me did not ease her pain. Watching one's child grow in another lodge would be the greatest gift but she would be filled with the largest pain she would ever know. Losing her husband was a grief that was hard to bare, however raising only one child now would have to be enough. Mother brought to Lucy the blankets and clothes that she had made for me, assuring her that the warmth of my blankets would keep me safe and they moved back to their own lodge. This would help Lucy prepare for me to leave with her and my brother. My mother fought her grief and tears inside of her.

My Aunt gathered Kati in an embrace and began to smile. She told my mother of the great joy she brought to her these many years. Her love for my mother was great even before she gave up her newborn child. She thanked my mother and then placed me back into my mother's arms. Aunt Lucy told all that were there that she could not bring herself to take her beautiful niece from her true mother. She then looked to my Uncle and they returned home. In the years that followed, I grew to know my Aunt well. She taught me all that she could and loved me like a mother. There were many nights that I would stay at their longhouse and enjoy their love and attention.

So proud I was to know that I would always have two mothers. I did not know I could come to love my mother any more than I already did. The sacrifices she was prepared to make for her family spread warmth all through my heart and I etched the story into the seams of my mind. One day I hoped to be able to show such a love for my family as my mother had shown us, in a time long ago.

These enjoyable days were cut short as the Unaka disease spread to Chota and Aunt Lucy became very ill. Much later in my life, I would learn that this killer disease was known as small pox. Attakullakulla was in Charlestown when the sickness came. The young ones were kept in their lodges to contain the spread of the spots that quickly became large sores. Little Owl had been staying with our Uncle while his father was away and quickly became as sick as Aunt Lucy and Oconostoa.

Word had been sent to my mother that my grandparents, Moytoy and Su Gi, were moving to a summer camp in the mountains. Far from the sickness that was quickly moving throughout the villages of Chota, Great Telico, and many other villages, they would be protected to carry on the legacy of our People.

It is hard to explain my gift of knowing, but among my people I am accepted and loved. The Unaka do not believe as we do, so we protect this knowledge from them. For as hard as we try to live with them, they do not want to live with us. I fear for my people, but within me I know that we will survive as a tribe; I have seen in visions my grandchildren living among the white man. I see rivers growing and becoming larger with many villages beside them. I see great clouds of smoke rising from their towns and cover them in a grayness that one cannot see through. These places smell as a dead thing.

What the Unaka did not understand was that we believed in the same Great Spirit/Creator/Yawa; they are all the same person. Furthermore, it did not make them see us differently once we joined their religion. My People tried to blend with the

Unaka, but are not accepted by the white skinned people, try as we may.

I came to understand many Unaka were forced to leave their lands because of the way they believe. They were loaded onto ships and sent to "The New Land." Now they have come to our land and claim it as their own. Could they not see that they were doing the same thing to my people as was done to them? How do they not see what they are doing? Hard as we try to live with them, they try only to take what is ours. Our lands and game become smaller and smaller with each passing season.

The way of my People is simple. When you work with what the Creator gives you, all things are better. Our lands are large and we must protect them to maintain our way of living. The Mohawk and the Creek often go to war with my people over the lands where we hunt and live. At one time, we had buffalo that ran in great herds but when they were hunted and thinned out we had to hunt smaller animals to feed our villages. Still, these animals were not put to waste but all they gave went to good use- even their bones. All things are done with reason. The approval of the Creator means everything to us. When the Creator becomes unhappy with us there is always a price to pay.

Ani Yunwiya are wise people. We have lived here for a hundred thousand years. These people who come to our land claim it as their discovery! Are we as a people to be pushed from our land and homes that we have loved and tended for these thousands of years? Knowing this to be so only saddens my heart further. Our people must be ready for what will someday be. The warnings I have for my people must wait for now. I wait for the Great Shepherd to show me when the time will be right to deliver a message that is breaking my heart. The future I see is not what I want for my children. I will use all of my gifts and knowledge to prepare the seeds of the future. As I lie full with child and now not able to care for myself, I can see clearly our way of life is good. Not the evil savages the Unaka claim us to be. If all would but leave us alone we would get along well without their beads and cloth they trade with us. Will one day they accept us for who we are? I feel overwhelming sadness when I think this way, for I am sure of the answer: "No." I feel sadness as I see we will never be accepted for who we are. In my visions I see we will be separated from our home land one day. I do know that I must continue to work for the good of the Cherokee as is my destiny. For this reason I was born upon this earth and in this time.

As I grew rounder with each passing day, all I could think of was Kingfisher and how he must be longing to return to our home, a home now even larger than when he left five full moons ago. I so hoped he would have returned by now. All I could do was eat and sleep. I could never tell where the sun or moon would be when I awoke. Kati was such a wonderful mother to me. She did all she could do for my comfort and prayed with me that this season would soon pass and that Kingfisher would return to us before our wee one was in my arms. My mother knew what it was to carry a child without the father present, and showed her love for me each day in the way she cared for me and the child that grew in my womb.

My dreams were the only place I have ever seen my father. Mother did not often speak his name, but she did say Longfellow reminded her of him. "He was FiveKiller of the Bird Clan," she had told us proudly. Kati never brought another man into her lodge after father died, not even when she was still a young, beautiful woman.

When Longfellow was but a little boy he would tell me that one day he would carry our fathers' name. Though he had been given many names in life, at the home of his mother he was

Longfellow. As a young warrior he became known as The Raven of Chota. When he moved to start his own town he became known only as The Raven. He took a wife with him to his new home by the Ocoee River. He had hopes and dreams of becoming a father, but they lost two children at birth. She finally became full with child again. This time she grew to such size that she could barely move. When her time of birthing came she grew very sick. She labored for two moons, but when the boy child came forth he was dead. Her pain did not ease and another son came forth and he was dead. Not long after the birth of the second son she fell into a sleep she never awoke from.

My brother stayed on in the village by the Ocoee River where he now felt he belonged. He wished to stay on in his own place as the women are the ones who inherit their mother's property. The men do not hold onto things so well as we women. So it is in the way of a matriarchal society. The French and English tried to change us into them by forcing us to take on their traditions. Their way is to allow the men to inherit all things, our ways are the opposite.

Though no women may be a Principal Chief, we may sit as a Chieftainess, with voting rights. In many tribes and other cultures, women are not held with much regard. My glee at being born Cherokee is great. The love I feel for my people is greater. The love I have for my family is rivaled by only one other, the love for my Creator. He is the one I talk to all through the day and give thanks to every night after we have laid down to sleep.

I sent word by a messenger to Kingfisher. The messenger was to tell him if he had not returned by the birth of our child I would set his belongings outside the longhouse, love, the skinny woman, so he knew my jest. This is, however, a true custom of the ending of a marriage among the Cherokee. This was my way of being playful with my husband; I would never do such a thing to him. His spirit would forever dwell inside my soul 'til I leave this world and go to another.

Though my time was getting nearer, no sign of him had I seen. I would go to sleep each night and hope for his return in the morning. Finally I was awakened by a ticklish feeling across my face. When I opened my eyes, my soul sang. He was there! He was strong of mind and splendid of body. No wounds could I see. He was filled with stories of their many triumphs, this man from the Deer Clan, my husband, Kingfisher. How I love saying his name. My husband's gift of white swan feathers lay around my bed mat. So happy I was of his return that I did not notice right away the breaking of the child's water until a chill overtook my body.

Kingfisher's heart is one of a warrior. As the pains of birth came and went, he could clearly see the pain in my face. Most men will not help with a birthing, but my husband was not like any other warrior. He sang love songs to me and our unborn child while tightly holding my hand. He wiped the sweat from my brow as I lay laboring to birth the seed of our love. It was near the end of my laboring that the Creator showed me the life of the little spirit that was soon to come forth.

We are proud to be Cherokee; we are a mighty nation of proud people. A people who try to do right by the land the Creator gave us and to the new little spirits we raise in our longhouses. The little ones of our clan are taught the way of the Ani Yunwiya, the Water People. We also know and teach them the importance of the seven clans of the tribe of the Cherokee, seven being the favored number of Yawa. The Shepherd who came to our lands long ago had taught us the way of love and peace. Yawa told us that one day he would return and that our names would be written down for all time. He told us that after we passed from this world we would come to dwell with him. He sent his winged spirits to live among us and to protect his beloved children.

These were the many things I have thought of during the many full moons that I lay full with child and not able to do my chores. I missed much the gathering of the medicines and our winter bounty. Being skilled in the use of herbs, I had seen many children born to the earth. Even though I knew what to expect, it still had not prepared me for the next full day of pain, a pain I had never known before. This pain would end in such sweet joy though, a joy greater than I had ever felt. As a healer I had seen this hope and love of a new mother as she holds her child for the first time and awaited my turn for the presence of my wee one.

Kingfisher would not leave my side. He told me stories of their battles and the many brave feats of our warriors. The Creek were also telling stories amongst other tribes. They spoke of the fierce warrior chief, Dragging Canoe and my Kingfisher. Together my cousin and husband were proving themselves an unbeatable force. I so wished I could have journeyed with them to see myself their triumphs and victories.

How sweet and gentle he was with me all through my hard laboring with our child. He tenderly fed me the broth with the helpful herbs that had been added to our cook pot to ease my pain. He gave me small sips of cool water, as not to make me ill. He wiped my brow tenderly with a cool cloth and softly sang songs of love to me and our wee one. These are the memories that would stay with me through a lifetime and beyond.

The Atawehi came to our longhouse to check on me and the unborn child. He tried swaying Kingfisher from staying at my side for so long, but he would not budge. Mother watched and smiled at his kind, gentle way.

Kati did as her mother SuGi had done for me at my birth, and went to the river to bathe my child when she finally arrived into the world and tribe of the Cherokee. My daughter's first bath took place in the same river, at the same place as mine had been. Once again, the White Wolf appeared. He came to my child's first ritual bath. Just as SuGi had done, my mother swore an oath to raise this child in the way of the Ancients.

When she returned from the banks of the Little Tennessee River, her eyes were filled with tears of gladness. Though my grandmother had waited until after my fifth year to tell my mother of the appearance of the White Wolf, Kati did not make the same choice with me. She came at once and told me the story of my child's first bath in the river, as I was too ill to join the bathing ritual. As she recounted the experience, we knew she too would one day do many great things for our People. I prayed she would not have to carry the knowing as I do or see things that she could not control. I knew it was not my place to judge what the Creator had in store for my children or my grandchildren that would one day come to this world.

The days began to move slowly for Kati and Kingfisher, for my time with child had taken a toll on my body and mind. The swelling of my hands and feet were signs of an illness that few of our women survived. I fell into a deep sleep-one my husband and mother feared I would never awake from. In the beginning my child would nurse from me in my sleep with my loving mother doing all she could to keep us both alive. Kati and the Atawehi were anxious of my child's health. They wanted to put a special mix of herbs into the broth that I would be fed, but such herbs are deadly to a newborn.

The Atawehi was sure I would pass from this life if the wee one continued to sup from my breasts. He told Kingfisher and

73

Kati that there was a mother in the next village that had lost her wee one and her milk still flowed.

There were many towns and villages in prayer to the Creator to spare my life and that of my child. So it was to be, a woman of the Bird Clan would be brought to live in our longhouse and feed my child which I was not able to do. Within days the child started to thrive and was finally growing with the milk of another mother. This allowed Kingfisher and Kati more time to care for my seemingly lifeless body.

The Atawehi came daily bringing any new herbs or ways of healing that he and other Medicine Men of other tribes could conger, though the swelling of my body did not lessen. My mother lovingly prepared lotions made of violets to keep my skin from drying and kept the sleeping sores from my body. The roles had switched and suddenly my community, my People, became the healers attempting to bring me back to life.

Longfellow, The Raven of Chota, came home a week after the birth of my daughter. With him he brought the healing water from the Magic Springs. This water has the power to heal if the Creator wishes it to be so. For the next two days I was given as much of this water from the Magic Spring as could be gotten in me.

They prepared teas of catnip that were seeped and laid upon my swollen hands and feet all throughout the day and night. The healing broth that had been made was also from the water of the spring and was fed to me often. On the third day after my brother's return with the water, the swelling in my hands started to be less. Then the next day the swelling from my feet started to leave also. After the fifth moon of my brother's return, I awoke from the deep and dreamless sleep that I had been in for so long. The Creator had chosen to spare my life. When I awoke it was to the sweet smell of the violet potion my mother had prepared and rubbed into my skin.

Kati proclaimed a miracle and sang and shouted throughout the town of Chota, telling all of my recovery and praising the Creator for sparing her daughter's life. Why, through my gift of knowing, had I not seen how gravely ill I was? Had the Creator spared me the pain of knowing? I chose to believe the latter.

Kingfisher gathered our child in his arms and came to lay with me. He spoke gently to me, "Beloved, it has been so long that you slept. My fear was great that you would not live to see our wee one grow. The Creator has watched over you both and brought you back from your lifeless sleep. I have prayed that you be spared to share a long life with me and our child. See, she has your eyes and shares the same tone of your skin. Now I have another rose to gaze upon. Your mother has never left your side. It is she who has had most of the burden of your care." He then laid our child gently into my arms.

"I have fought in many battles and felt no fear, but these many moons I have been scared to lose you. Why, beloved did you not send word that you were so ill?" he asked.

The words came slowly from lack of use "My husband, fear not, the Creator has sent me home to you and our family. He has yet a purpose for me in this life. My destiny has yet to be fulfilled. I will soon be strong again."

The three of us fell asleep there together, my child and I held close in the arms of my warrior.

These many moons that I lay ill, my daughter still did not have a name. Kingfisher waited for me to recover my strength before mentioning that our child still bore no name of her own. Wee One was what they called her through my time of sleep; not a fitting name for such a beautiful little spirit the Creator had sent us. As the days and weeks continued, I grew stronger and aware of how similar my daughter was to my mother. We decided their names should be the same. Little Kati, Kingfisher and I were a family now.

While we are young, many of our destinies are decided by the Elders and the Wise Ones. The Elders study our children so they can gain the knowledge of what our children should be trained for.

My cousin, Dragging Canoe, who was known as Little Owl in his youth, received his name after his actions as a young brave. He was determined to join in on an active war party, but his father, Attakullakulla, would not allow him to join in a war raid against the Muscogee Creek, telling him he was not yet strong enough a warrior to move as the other warriors did. To prove his readiness to join in the war party he dragged his canoe for an extremely long distance. When his father heard what his son had done he was given the name of Dragging Canoe.

It was around this same time, that I also received my new name, "Nanyehi" (one who is walks with the spirits), which replaced my birth name of Wild Rose.

There were many name changes for many different reasons. For instance, a warrior named "Runner" could outrun all people in our village as well as most of the men of the other clans. My mother changed her name to Tame Doe after she adopted a young doe and raised it to a full grown deer. Amongst our People, my mother is mostly known as Kati but she still loved the correlation of her gentle new name. Changing names as people change and grow into who they are to become is a common practice among the tribes of the land.

Little Kati not only looked the same as my mother but also tended to be like her in her sweet nature. It was clear to all who gazed upon her that they both share a like spirit of love and tenderness. Our wee one was truly one of the water people. For every morning that we went to bathe in the stream, my daughter kicked and squealed with glee and happiness in the cool, slow, moving water. It is our way, but not all enjoy the bathing ritual as much as we do. I do not think it is coincidence that she enjoys the water more than most, for she was conceived in a waterfall where her father and I first made love.

It was so good to have Kingfisher by my side the first full moons after our daughter came to dwell in our world. In was in this time after Kati's birth, I began to feel the ache for my husband's love. Tame Doe said that I need not rush, though she understood the longing for a man. Kingfisher was patient with my healing time, a time that my body needed much rest to recover from Little Kati's birth.

I was sure there would be a son for Kingfisher, but I knew not when. Kingfisher needed the rest also. Although he returned to me unharmed, he was very tired from the many moons of warring with the Creek, then his constant care for me and Little Kati. Through the many moons of not knowing if we would live or die, he suffered much.

We sat by the fire many nights as he recited stories of his many battles. Kingfisher, Chief Oconostoa, Dragging Canoe, and the other war chiefs spent much time making plans for battle. These chiefs have seen many battles, together they planned and made ready our warriors for the survival of the Cherokee Nation.

The longer these wars went on, the weaker we would all become in the end. The day would come that all Tribes of all the

Indian Nations of America will be forced to come together for the good of all, to fight for our survival as a race of a people.

We tell these stories to the children so they will remember for all time what their ancestors did for the survival of all. The Unaka were coming by the scores of many numbers upon fleets of boats from the King's country far across the sea. Some came because of religious beliefs, some to be in a new land that was wild and mysterious, a land that could be taken for little or nothing. Some countries released people from their burgeoning prisons and were sent to our land to free their countries of the burdens of their care.

How odd the way of the Unaka – to keep bad men alive, and send them where they continue with their bad ways. As a way of never forgetting the past, and for our survival, these stories must go on so that we may carry on far into the future. We are told these stories of our past many times so that we forget not our old ways and the people who sacrificed their lives for the survival of all.

We have had to war with many other countries as well as the Unaka. The Spaniards tried to conquer us, the Vikings came with their large, odd-shaped ships, the French set about trying to remove us from our lands that we love and care for. But the new Americans grew bolder and stronger.

Kingfisher and I walked the village together visiting the longhouses of our families. We watched the young ones play stick ball and the pole game. The hours spent playing games were vital for training their minds and bodies. The pole game taught the boys and girls to get along well together and also trained their muscles to be strong and limber. Swimming in the rivers taught our bodies to be strong and swift as well. The playing of the stick game taught the boys to think swiftly on their feet and strengthened their bodies. The elders and wise ones would watch them play closely and choose who would be the hunters, the warriors, the farmers, the healers, or even a future leader.

As we watched the children at play, Kingfisher looked over at me and said, "With you my beloved woman, I wish to have many children. They will carry our seed forward for many, many years to come, for all time in this land."

The days turned into seasons and Kingfisher and I grew closer as a family. Because my husband is a skilled hunter and warrior of the Deer Clan, we ate well. The Creek warriors had not been invading our lands as much these days, but we were always prepared to send war parties to defend our lands when needed.

Through many long nights of winter we sat with the Elders listening to the stories of the great hunts and dangerous wars of long ago. The times of these great hunts were long gone, but we could not allow the younger ones to forget them.

The settlers and traders would send the hides of the buffalo across the ocean to lands far away. These hides and others were much sought after by many. Cherokee as well as these other places traded the skins of the buffalo and that of the deer, raccoon, beaver, mink and even the wolf and fox. At one time our land teemed with many of these animal spirits, but with the greed of many of my own tribe as well as the Unaka their numbers seemed to become smaller and smaller each season.

Our most honored animal is the wolf; but lately they were being murdered in large scores. They were not only killed for their fur but because they were seen as an enemy. The Cherokee as well as other nations could not take the spirit of the wolf easily. The people of the Wolf Clan, by right of the land, are the only People that may kill the wolf.

I watched as my mother began to grow older before me. Her shining black hair now had a small streak of silver down one side and I wondered if one day my hair would be this way. I prayed that my father was proud of the way we lived our lives and will welcome us with pride when we meet him on the other side.

My mother is very beautiful and was known in her youth for her great beauty. Many visitors told stories in lands faraway of her loveliness. Her brothers, who sailed for six moons to see a King, told stories in that land of her way with animals and of her talent with herbs and healing.

While in England, my uncles were amazed at what they saw and learned. They were young and only knew women like their sister and mother. Women in England did not act like the women of their tribe. The women in this far-off land were different; they would spend much of the day preening in front of a looking glass, and applying powders that changed the way they looked. They would ride around in fancy wagons in their finest attire going seemingly nowhere, and their soft-skinned hands were covered by gloves, not knowing a day of work. My uncles knew how important our women were, that our villages thrive from the work that we do.

These many years with no husband have been hard on my Mother. Kati always worked hard to provide for my brother and me, but her brothers always saw to our needs. Mother became lonely while Attakullakulla, her twin and lightening soul, was so far away from her when they visited that far-off land. They came to this world during a terrible spring storm, so fierce that the story of their birth was told by the fire; born to the mighty Chief Moytoy two screaming babies that held to each other tightly as the lightening crashed and struck the ground in double strikes throughout the village. They had never been parted from each other so long a time. Nor would they ever be again, except by death. My mother and uncle shared as the soul of one, it was as if the one could feel the others pain, and they could speak from one's mind to the other's.

She told stories all my life about how our People came to be in this land, a land with game and water a plenty. We are taught from a young age that the People are put on this land by the Great Creator for a purpose: to follow him and protect His land. My grandmother SuGi taught Tame Doe (Kati), who in turn taught me, and we will teach my daughter, Little Kati, and the spirits of the wee ones that are to follow her.

Our Ancient ones told us the stories of how the bow and arrow were first made. We have improved much on these weapons over these many years, but the making of these bow and arrows helped the number of our People grow by many. The only thing greater than the bow and arrow to us is fire.

Our Ancient Ones tell the story of how the Creator sent His original People fire. He sent a great storm. During this storm, there was much lighting sent from the sky. The lighting struck a large tree and began a great fire. The priests lit a fire from the tree. Since this time the flame at Red Clay has always been kept burning and is the source from which we relight our fires anew each year.

We had great fields of maize that the women of our village tended to so that we had food in the cold season. The white settlers have called our maize "corn." We have learned to fashion great jars of clay for storing of maize and other food we dry. In these jars we also placed dried nuts, meats and berries for our winter meals and the healthiest of seeds we would sow come the spring.

We built food huts near to our winter lodges. They were built high in the air to keep the bear and deer from our stored foods. By keeping our food off the ground it did not spoil so fast, and would last until the earth bore the fruits of a new season. We have done these things in this way since the time of the Ancients.

The Cherokee People have come far on this earth with no help from the Unaka, who like to say that our ways are wrong. If they are so wrong, then why have we grown into so many? We knew their ways were different from ours, but even still we learned many of their ways and recognized some were useful. I wished they could see the good in ours.

When the Unaka first came to our land, we thought they were ghost people and we treated them with kindness and saved them from starvation many times. The ghost people did not come prepared to survive in our lands. We invited them to our corn ceremonies and taught them our way of growing maize, beans, and squash and the ways we survived.

We did not own the land or the sky above it; it was given to us by the Creator. We did not own the water that ran through our land, but it gave us food and clean water for drinking, cooking, and bathing. We are the Ani Yawia, the Water People.

I saw visions in my dreams.

A day was shown to me when they put great walls across the rivers and changed the way the river was born to run. The Creator designed them one way, a way they will soon no longer be. I saw the land where my Chota lies in the smoke of time and I knew one day it would be no longer.

These I have kept to myself, for what is the good of sharing something that is destined to be? There is no way of altering what is to be.

As we prepared to move to the winter house, our lives became very busy. I enjoyed the happy days leading up to winter with my little family, but we had to move what we needed to our winter dwelling and prepare for the cold season. In some ways, I looked forward to settling into this season of rest from our chores and also to the time of our closeness as a family. It was not often that wars were fought during the winter season.

Some tribes moved to the South where the weather is much warmer than the village of Chota in the cold season. However, most of my family stays in Chota. With food plentiful, we do not have to move like other tribes of our Woodland brothers. Some of our elderly go south towards the sea, as their bones do not hurt so much from the coldness of the season.

The days become shorter with the cold of winter and we spent much of our time in our winter house as it was easy to warm. Our fires were started each year anew from the eternal flame of the Cherokee. The Embers are brought from Red Clay to each home and the fires were restarted and remained burning until the same time the next year.

As long as this flame burnt, our people would survive. This flame was always tended to by the people who lived in Red Clay, our sacred meeting place to the south. There are many sentinels that stand watch over this sacred place. Each year, we met there at the place of the sacred eternal flame. It had been a place of gathering for as far into the smoke of time that anyone could remember. It is here our clans gathered to exchange stories and ideas that would strengthen the Cherokee Nation.

This was also the place of the Mystic Hole. It was truly a special place where the water comes from between the rocks, the place where the Great Spirit gave to us the cleanest, clearest water. The water was hauled back to the village by any means; this was where our Cherokee ponies work hardest for the People. This water was used by the Medicine Man and our spiritual leaders. The medicine man used this water to make medicine and the black tea that was used in many of our ceremonies. We believe that when someone becomes sick, it is because they have done something wrong or angered one of the animal spirits, or they have passed judgment on someone unjustly. I, however, do not believe this. Alas, this I have also kept to myself.

The Creator has given me peace in my heart and the knowing that this is not true. I know that we are safe and will one day walk alongside Him. The ancient ones made pictures on the cave walls and through time we saw how it was when the man surrounded in light came to our land. The Creator sent The Great One to show us the way of good, not always can we see the right of the other and it will lead to fighting. We believe in the one true Creator and that we are safe in his presence. The Unaka call this being a "Christian," but do not agree with our ways. Why can they not see we are Christian too?

As the winter wore through, we began to see signs that we would have an early spring and we knew the time was growing near to move back into the longhouses and start our planting for the new growing season. We culled out the largest and strongest of the seeds from our yearly crops to plant in our fields the next season as they produce the most bountiful plants. This job was done mostly by the women and girls of the village to the north of Chota.

Up off the banks of the river were our growing fields. The area was flat and easier to guard. We grew maize and squash and berries for eating and medicine. Juices from these fruits were even used for dyes, as we waste nothing. For what the

Great Spirit asks of us is that we not waste anything that He gives us for our use. The Great Creator who gives all can take all.

Near where we grew our crops was the place we used for stick ball and other games. This is where our visitors are welcome to set their camps. Many times land and property are won and lost in these fields. We have a passion for stick ball and some are willing to risk all that they have in the spirit of the game.

As the many seasons passed with Kingfisher, I felt as if life was perfect. Little Kati was strong and healthy. She learned quickly and was the delight of her father's eye. Mother's health was good and we knew many seasons of peacefulness.

Dragging Canoe was not as peaceful at this time, however, and leery of all Unaka. He continued to be a force to be reckoned with. His father, Attakullakulla, the great peace maker and grandson of the mighty Chief Moytoy, was now a chosen War Chief led by his uncle, Chief Oconostoa. Dragging Canoe's life had many directions.

I was glad to see that Little Kati showed no sign of the gift of knowledge. She was happy to do her chores with the other women and girls of the village and showed no signs of having the knowing that I was given. Parts of me wished that she had inherited my gift of knowing, but life would be easier for my daughter than it was for me without it. Little Kati would not have to feel the hurt of knowing and seeing the plights of others. To feel the pain of others is the hardest part of the gift the creator has given to me. There are times that I see or relive a time that has passed and feeling this pain over and over is wearing upon one's soul. She would not have to look into people's eyes and deny them any truths. She would not have to interpret her dreams or the dreams of others.

Much of my time was still spent in the gathering of herbs, roots, berries, and honey for the making of many medicines. The bees ate of the flowers and we ate of the honey comb. We have long used this sweet liquid to sweeten our breads and food. The honey given from the bees also protected our heads from aches. All things have their use. When possible, I still hunted with my husband or a small band of huntresses. But my most important role was still counselor to my People. Though I prayed for peace amongst all people of all Nations, I continued along with Kingfisher to follow our principal ruling chiefs, Attakullakulla or Oconostoa in doing whatever necessary. During times of peace, Attakullakulla ruled our People. During times of war, Oconostoa would lead our People. Like everything else on the land, every person has their gift and usefulness.

Our People have endured much for as far back as our stories go. We are a beautiful people, the Cherokee. Our clans worked together for the good of the tribe for we knew we were strongest together. Warring with the Creek and our other enemies lessened for a few seasons. We stayed strong in our belief that the Great One controls all and protects His people.

My warrior, my husband, followed the orders of our chiefs and had shown himself to be a great leader with skills rivaled by few. Much is called for from those who do things well. The demands of the People seem to make me more tired with each request made. My visions and dreams told me many things to come that I did not understand.

It is the Great Creator that still rules my heart and mind, but it did not quiet the fear I had for my People. This fear was rooted in my heart as a great oak is rooted in the ground. My soul sang sad songs for many of my visions.

My prayers to the Great One were for peace for all families of my clan and tribe. For the safety of Kingfisher and Little Kati and for the health of my mother, wisdom for my uncles Attakullakulla, Oconostoa and my cousin Dragging Canoe. I prayed also for the Unaka that have settled close to our lands for it is good to pray for those that would harm you. I asked that the Great Spirit would soften their hearts and minds to accept and understand us and our ways. I prayed for my brother, the Raven, who still lives near the Ocoee River that he be kept safe from our enemies.

I prayed that the rain would come in warm seasons, and when the winter season came I prayed that it will not be so cold that people and animals and land died. I prayed for the animal spirits that fed and clothed us, that they would be happy in the hunting grounds, for they are gifts of life to our people. My heart sang with joy as my family had been blessed with good health and wealth. The days had been many since Kingfisher had to make war. The times of peace were certainly the sweetest.

I prayed all these blessings continued to be so, though I had been having a vision that frightened me. I kept this fear to myself for I did not wish to alarm Kingfisher. I remember this season of cold well, for I feared this would be the last winter of my life. Of this I was sure for the vision showed me life was coming to an end and I could no longer see my name on the smoke of time. Things had been so peaceful that I did not want this time to change. I saw my husband with the wind blowing through the feathers of an eagle that were tied in his hair. He took me into his arms and my world went black. In this vision I fear I have seen my own death even though I do not know why or how. The knowing is at times difficult, especially when it is about one's self.

Our days began early in the stream in which we bathed. This is the way I love to start my day and would do so even if our law did not demand it. At the setting of the sun, we watched as the warm rays filtered through the trees that grew upon the mountains and watched as the rays of the setting sun sparked and flickered on the waters of the river. I could spend the rest of our days in this way, for at this moment I felt safe from all harm.

We watched as the ponies and their foals grazed in our valleys and meadows while playing with their young. These ponies had many uses in the village and helped ease our burdens. We seldom used our ponies for war purposes as they could not get through the thick forest as well as a warrior would on foot and are not of much use in the treacherous mountains. The Unaka and their slaves made large pathways that must be cleared of all trees. These roads were watched by many renegades looking for easy prey. So we used the ways of the Ancients and went by foot the natural paths that had been made by deer and other animals. There were times when the Ancient ways were much better than the new ways.

Our crops were many that year and we had stored much food for winter. As we once again settled in for the cold season, I longed to play the basket games and spend time with Kati telling her stories that have been passed down. One story I would tell was of how the Creator made man and how man became lonely, the Great Spirit then planted maize from which a woman came forth. This was how man got woman and why we honor the harvesting of the maize.

When the first signs of spring began to come, I knew that I carried another child for Kingfisher. I had prayed much that this child would be born for his father Kingfisher. He so wanted a son to train in the way of the warrior. I wanted to tell him of the gift that I carried inside, but held this to myself to focus on Little

Kati who was growing in the way of the People and her clan, that of the Wolf.

A messenger arrived from Red Clay with news that an urgent council meeting had been called. He brought news that made my belly quiver with fear. I saw the light of my husband's eyes change quickly for he also knew this news was bad, news of War with the Creeks.

The week that followed was full with preparation for a war party. I could hear the shattering of the peace we had known for these many seasons. My mind rushed to sort through what must be done before the war party left. Though they did not know it, they would be joined by another warrior: me. The warriors would be leaving after the full moon, which meant I had only three moons to prepare.

With no one the wiser, I had to be ready to depart with the warriors secretly. The only thing I could think of was going to war with Kingfisher, regardless of the danger at hand; I could not be apart from him again. I knew he would not allow me to go if I asked. I was mindful to use care with my words showing no signs of preparation for travel, and being careful to not let slip that his seed was growing inside me. I knew that if he were to know of these things there would be no reasoning with him and he would not allow me to join this war party.

From the time of our Little Kati's birth, Kingfisher had been very protective of us. There were many things he would ask me not to do. War Parties were small and led by the younger, lesser chiefs so my warrior could stay home more. The hunting away from Chota was done by large hunting parties, the winters had been mild and the herds of deer were of good number so I did not have to go out and hunt as often. Our parting was little and our love grew to great strength.

If I understood my vision, it might be the last of my days. If I was to leave this world it would be at my husband's side. The time I spent with my Little Kati was being stored in my mind. My mother, brothers, and Kingfisher would watch over her if my days should be at an end. The vision came again and the end was still the same. My heart wept for I loved my daughter and husband with all that I am.

On the day that Kingfisher was to depart, our morning bath in the creek was special. There was no dew on the earth this morning and warmth grew within us as we joined as one in the creek.

He said, "There was another time not long ago we joined in a waterfall and the Creator blessed us with Little Kati. Now beloved, my seed you will carry again. We are in need of a son skinny woman," he whispered in my ear.

"Aye," I giggled, "maybe so." I paused and said; "My husband is sure of himself." My husband puffed out his chest with pride as he was indeed so sure of himself.

Then he said, "I am sure of only one thing: I will love you for all time, my wife, and you will carry my son," a smile crossed his full lips.

As we continued to dress, my heart beat as fast as a frightened deer. So loud it beat, I was sure he knew my secret, one of many I now carried with me each day. As my mind swirled, I knew what I was planning was the will of the Creator. Only when the Creator lays his hand upon me am I able to perform all the tasks that must be done to complete His will and feel His peace in my heart.

I prayed that I would be able to tell someone, but I did not know for sure whom to trust with this information. The danger in helping me with this might not be worth the trouble it could cause to whom I asked. I could not think of anyone to help me so I prayed to the Creator to show me all that would be needed on this journey that I was to make.

I grieved at the thought of the son I carried, for he would not know life. So strong was my drive to protect Kingfisher that nothing else mattered. My life I would give for my husband and family.

The day we bade the war party farewell, I told my mother I had special chores to attend to and would be gone through the night. I told her not to worry as I was going to the mountain where the Atawehi dwelt. I was to help the Medicine Man collect special roots, herbs and berries for potions to be used in the upcoming ceremonies. The early spring had brought many fruits and berries ahead of their season, so this could be easy for her to believe.

As quickly as possible, I collected the prepared supplies that were waiting for me. I had hidden them in the bushes along the trail the war party would follow and knew I had to move swiftly to catch up with them. Since my day as a child when I was lost in the Smoking Mountains, I have learned much.

The training from my youth insured that if I should be lost again, I would be as prepared as any seasoned warrior and care for myself. The many hunting and war parties I had been on before my uniting with Kingfisher taught me all that was needed to help keep me safe. Now, more than ever, I would be in need of every skill I had learned in all my years upon this land.

Moving as swiftly as my legs would allow, I ran for what seemed hours. I moved as swiftly and quietly as I could, taking breaks only when my body betrayed me. My legs hurt from lack of water. My thirst was great and my stomach cried for food, but I ran on. There was great need to catch up with the war party before nightfall if possible. The further south I journeyed, the more safety became a concern. Other tribes had many spies and runners on our lands watching our activities as well as the Creek to report back to their chiefs. We too had spies and sentinels hidden amongst the forests and mountains of our land as well as our enemy's land. Some unlucky hunters and trappers had been killed by these lone scouts. I was not going to be one of those.

Seldom were women killed, but dressed as a Woman Warrior I would be considered a man and thus slain as one. My family would be greatly saddened if I met such an end, but if I could die protecting my husband, a good death it would be.

As the sun began to set behind the mountains, I had to slow down and take more care with each step. The night continued to darken with the hiding moon, and I caught sight of a small Creek hunting party heading in the same direction as our warriors.

Feeling unsure of my safety, I bedded down in a grove of pine where I ate and drank. The fallen needles of the pines made a soft, warm bed and I rubbed my sore legs and feet before falling into a deep sleep. I heard nothing, not the owl brothers or the cats that walk the night.

The soundless night came to an end as I awoke startled by my dreams. Again, a knowing came upon me. I knew that the lives of my family would soon be changed and for this I was sad, but nothing would get in my way of protecting the man I had dreamt about so long and loved so deeply. A life without Kingfisher I could not see, but a life without me is what the future held in my vision for I saw the darkness of death.

I lay silent for a time watching and praying for the day ahead. Bathing would have to wait this day. I spotted a wolf with her pups playing not far from where I had slept. My eye caught movement to my right side. Sighing with relief I saw that the White Wolf was again with me. I greeted him with my eyes showing that I was thankful for his ever-watching presence.

The child I carried would go with me to the place the Creator promised, a place where peace reigns for the rest of time and where fear and sickness cannot come: the place of eternal rest which I have so craved.

After prayer and a small meal of dried venison, I arose and ran from the warmth of the pine needles where I had spent the night. It was nearly dawn, yet I felt I must move on in hopes of staying near the main party of warriors and yet not be seen. Once Kingfisher found out what I had done, he would surely send me back to Chota. This, I was sure, could not happen; for my destiny was to be as I have envisioned with my beloved.

By late afternoon I was sure I had caught up with the war party. I saw the tracks on the ground, yet I stayed back. I felt something was not right. My spirit guide led me to a small ledge on the side of the mountain where I rested, ate, and drank. The day had been long and my legs were beginning to swell and ache again.

While I nestled there in this small place, I heard the movement of many feet and knew this was not the way of our warriors. I pulled in tight and held my breath for what seemed like more time than I could bear. Once the footsteps passed by, I moved to take a look; there were nearly a hundred warriors moving up the hillside. If I were to move, I would surely be seen. I began praying for their eyes to be shut to my presence so I could make my way to our warriors with the news of this war party at their flank.

I knew I must move with the swiftness of the deer, the quietness of a soaring eagle, and have the strength of a bear to reach my destiny. This knowing could save many of our warriors from death - and my husband was among them.

As I traveled through this night, my mind could not rest. I had to continue so I could warn Kingfisher and Dragging Canoe

93

of the enemy's large presence on our land. As the dawn approached, I saw the spirit people from my youth when I was lost in the Smoking Mountains standing before me with the Great White Wolf at their side. They were the same as they were when I was young. They fed me and gave me a sweet warm drink and pointed me toward home, the way to my people. Then they also pointed the way to the war party and told me to decide which path was to be true for me. They told me there was no time. You must choose which road to travel, the white road of peace or the red road to war. You must not fail, for to do so means the end of our time. Step into you, do not search of something that you are, you are that you be. I chose the path of war, the way to the South and West.

Before the noon sun warmed the land, I approached the camping war party who was preparing to eat a lunch of dried meats and berries. As I entered the camp, all became silent. Every man's eyes were upon me. I watched Kingfisher rise from where he sat with the other war chiefs, there was a fire that was lit in his dark eyes - a look I had never seen before. Walking the last few steps to my husband, a fear came upon me that I had never known. My eyes welled and from them I cried great tears that wet my face. I suddenly became weak as a newborn fawn and collapsed at his feet.

"What is it you do here woman?" he spoke harshly. The look upon his face softened as he lifted me to my weary legs.

Once I was standing firmly and had found my voice I answered, "I have come to warn you my husband, you are being followed by many enemy warriors." I told them all I had learned and saw in the nights before.

Kingfisher asked sternly, "You are brave my beloved, but tell the rest. How is it you come to be here?"

"My husband, long ago you told me you would not stand in my way of what I have been called upon to do by the Great Spirit. You would never interfere with the work the Creator had for me." I gazed into his eyes and asked firmly, "Is this not true?" As I saw his eyes soften, I knew all would be well and that he would come to understand that I did what I must.

The Chiefs had decided to split the warriors into two separate war parties. I, of course, was to go with Kingfisher. He told Dragging Canoe that as his warrior woman, I would fight alongside of him. Dragging Canoe had become a Great War Chief and I fully trusted the plans that Kingfisher, Oconostota, and Dragging Canoe put into place.

Kingfisher and I continued on with his party of warriors. As we neared the river some of the warriors slipped off towards the banks to hide among the brush and fallen trees. Half our number would be hidden by the river and would swim towards the battle sight. While we kept on the move by way of the deer paths that had been scouted ahead by our trackers, we allowed the Creek scouts to follow safely from behind. They would report our number as fewer, allowing for the surprise attack of the warriors that were hidden near and in the Etowah River. Runners were already in the lower villages, asking them to join in our fight; we knew we would need more warriors and braves if we were we to be the victors as we were outnumbered by scores. The French soldiers were well among their numbers, they had enlisted men from other tribes as well as renegades. This war was fast becoming something we had not prepared for.

We tried to stay from war with our Creek brothers to the south but could no longer accept their raids upon our towns and villages. They would be ready for our approach, of this we were sure. If the Creator wished my vision to come to fruition here, I would join Him soon.

Along the way we saw many signs of movement coming from differing directions. The Creeks were continuing to grow in number with the passing of each hour. The faith in our way of war is great; the most skilled of our clan were among our numbers. Retreating now could not be. With us into this battle we took much knowledge in the way of war.

We moved swiftly and carefully. My prayers never ceased that the Creator would clear our way to victory. I was sure the next day would bring the spilling of much blood upon the lands of the Creek and the Cherokee. The Creator from whom my knowing came had shown me the Ani Yuawia would be the victors. This battle would ensure the Creek would stay far away from our hunting grounds.

The place that we were now headed had once been known for being host to many games of stick ball. Land and many possessions had been lost and won on this land that we came to. There were times of peace and joy here where the blood of our peoples would soon flow. My prayer had always been for peace, but for these next days there would be no peace until the war was fought and won.

The Great Spirit moves in ways we do not always understand or know the purpose of. I prayed the reason we would be the victors of this war would be to regain peace in the land. If we could send the Creek from our lands, the French would loosen their foothold and maybe they would return to their own lands.

I was sure my family would survive for many years into the smoke of time. In these days to come, I envisioned my son and I walking into the loving arms of our Creator. My work was coming to an end in this life, but was to begin anew in a place of peace and love where we feel no pain and serve only our Creator.

There would be little sleep this night. While the moon was hidden in the clouds above I rested in the arms of my husband for on the morrow I would rest in the arms of the Creator.

We stopped and set camp not far from Ball Ground in Georgia. We ate from the dried meat and fruits prepared for this journey. Warriors took turns watching through the night. After the set of the moon we planned to be on the trail to war.

Kingfisher woke me from a restless sleep. He tenderly kissed me till he began to feel my kisses back to him. We lay for a while in each other's arms, listening to the drum of our hearts as they beat in the same rhythm. We arose and gathered together for our last words of planning for this day of war.

Before the rise of the sun we moved to the southeast of the Etowah River, crossing at a narrow, shallow area in a sharp bend in the river. After our party of warriors crossed we were joined by the braves who had been left behind up river and moved into position. This group of warriors attacked from the place we waited, where we joined as a mighty people to fight as one. We could not let the Creek or any Nation of this country - or another country for that matter - break us apart. For were this to happen, it would set brother against brother, which would break the strength of ties together. We held this position until the other parties could join our force. There was to be no turning back, though the Creek war party behind us grew larger with each passing hour.

"We have walked into a trap of our own setting," Kingfisher stated sadly. "Woman, we knew of the Creek spies that were following us. I was scouting throughout the darkness of night. Before the dawn I spotted the White Wolf, but I could not see my skinny wife who hid from all. The Great White Wolf showed himself to me and in doing so hid you from my eyes. I saw but I could not see. I cannot question the will of Yawa, or how you came to be here at this time."

"This day, my beloved," he continued, "you are to stay at my side and not be seen. I will not have you hurt in any way. The Creator and I will guard over your safety, that you may return to our daughter and your mother to raise many children to be strong and faithful Ani Yunwiya and care for many little wolf cubs." He pulled me close into his strong arms.

As the light began to crack across the sky our warriors moved into place. We moved as one, making no sounds of advance. We were sure that we were being watched, just as we were watching them. This morning there was no smoke from the little people, they were still. The deer did not go to the river that morning. Even the birds in the sky stayed silent and hidden from view. It was as if the world had gone still and all I could hear was my heart as it beat; I felt my blood pulse noisily through my veins.

When the cry of war sounded, all stillness changed in a moment of time. The Creek and their allies came from everywhere in mass. Had I not seen this with my own eyes I could not have believed such a sight could occur. All around me warriors were falling to the ground dead. We advanced slowly from the banks of the river across a meadow where I had once watched the stick games being played. How different it was now, covered in blood from fighting and anger not in jest.

As the day lengthened, Kingfisher found a deep swell of roots underneath a large oak tree in which we stayed. The fighting was fierce; many had fallen on both sides. Runners had been sent back from the village with more braves to fight this battle as we were still outnumbered ten to one. The skills of our warriors were mighty and great, but such odds as these were not good. I chewed on the bullets which were being shot from

Kingfishers mussawacon and reloaded them as quickly as I could.

I again prayed that we would be able to survive until more warriors could join from other clans and villages of the Cherokee Nation. The braves and warriors fought on throughout all of the morning and into the day, not moving forward from the spot where we had now fought for so long.

The war cries around us were loud and strong on both sides, enemies face to face fighting for land, fighting for larger hunting ground and simply fighting for the sake of war. Could they not see peace was best for all? My heart cried out for peace, but I continued to fight on alongside my husband.

After another hour had passed, we heard the call for retreat. But, I thought, Cherokee warriors never quit! Retreat from a war, a war that could cost us much in the way of land and had already cost us countless lives? This could not be!

Kingfisher looked into my eyes and held my face in his hands. "My beloved wife, I have put you in far too much danger and I fear I will not be able to protect you. Forgive me."

I tried to tell him with my eyes what my voice did not want to say. I began, "You my beloved husband have done all that you can. If it is my time of passing I would only pray to spend my last moments with you, for at my end all I want is to look into your eyes and then those of our Creator."

"Nanyehi," he uttered, "my beloved, I will not let you die at the hands of these dogs. Stay hidden here till I signal you to move," and I obeyed. Our muskets were loaded and ready; we would do this together. Kingfisher slowly rose from his spot to scout our retreat, he signaled for me to follow him low and to the right. As quietly and smoothly as I could I began to move to the right. I had moved only steps from where we had been pinned for half the day, not far above the banks of the stream that lead to the river. As I moved, I was taken to the ground by a searing pain in my left side. I looked up towards where Kingfisher knelt and watched as he lunged towards the spot where I lay.

"Nanyehi!" he yelled. He moved toward me and the warrior who had thrown his club at me. The warrior was close enough to scalp me with the blade he held aloft. A strange look ran across my attacker's face - this warrior recognized who I was and to whom he had just raised his war knife. My name and face are well known throughout the Creek Nation and the markings on my hands told of my power and status. The honor of my position was respected throughout all the eastern tribes. To strike or harm me in any way would cause great dishonor.

The warrior, quickly realizing his error, picked up his war club that lay at my side and ran toward the safety of his number. He wanted to protect himself against the wrath of the Great Spirit. He would later realize that not only had my life been spared that day but his life as well. To have killed a holy woman would surely have caused his end.

Swiftly Kingfisher reached me and lifted me up to him in an embrace and looked into my eyes with great love. Then- just as quickly as he had lunged for me- his head jerked toward his left shoulder and we started to fall to the ground. The wind caught the eagle feather tied in his hair and it lifted as if in flight, and he stared at me. I watched as the light of my husband's spirit left his eyes, as he fell to his death, covering my body with his. My world went black.

I felt the weight of my lifeless husband as he lay upon me. I held still, holding the warmth of his body, warmth I would never know again. I could hear the sounds of the grieving spirits as I lay pinned to the ground. "Ai ye," rang in my ears and then tore through my mind.

It was some time before I realized the piercing noise was in fact my own screams I was hearing. It was he that was to die and all I could feel or see was blackness. How had I not understood this? Were we both meant to die here on this day together? Questions ran through my mind as a new feeling took over. I would not leave this world without avenging my husband's death. I would fight for our people as Kingfisher had done throughout his life.

As I arose from the place where my husband lay dead, a great cry came from somewhere deep inside my soul - the battle cry known by all warriors and braves. I would fight to avenge the death of not only my beloved Kingfisher, but also that of his brothers and cousins that lay dead around me. A lone enemy warrior off to my right raised his gun to fire upon me, but I was quicker. My bullet sought his eyes and there found its target; he fell dead to the ground as I jumped over his body. I screamed the battle cry as it made me feel alive. I knew unbelievable sorrow would overtake my soul if I could not avenge the death of my Kingfisher; I had to live long enough to avenge the shred of life I had left as well.

It was as though I stepped out of time and watched as chaos surrounded me. Blood and weapons and bodies littered the ground around me. The Spirit People guided my every move as the strength of the White Wolf ran by my side as I dodged, rolled, jumped, and kicked my way through many warriors, killing them one by one.

From somewhere behind me, I felt the pounding of running feet. My people, the warriors of the Cherokee, were following me. Pride filled my veins where blood once ran. Going forward, away from the body of my love, I felt his spirit running through me. I felt my muscles strengthen and pulse with a power I did not know dwelled within me. We went forward and we fought on. Together, we won this war.

When the fighting finally ended, my mind became crazy with grief. A pain so deep, I thought my heart would shrivel up and die. So sure was I that it was me that was going to pass to the land of the Creator that I had not prepared myself for his loss. Why had I not been the one to go? Kingfisher was my world and I did not wish to walk upon this land without him.

The journey back to Chota was long and hard. I would not allow them to leave Kingfisher near the battle ground, yet I did not know where I wanted his body to rest. All I knew was it could not stay in this far off place, so close to the land of our enemy and so far from our beloved Chota.

So we went on toward Chota, a place where I was now to live without my husband. How could I explain to our Little Kati what happened to her beloved father? How would I begin to tell her that her father died protecting me and yet I still walked the land?

Knowing I was supposed to be there did not provide comfort for my aching heart. The Creator commanded that I go, yet my heart wished it ended differently. One day I know all will be revealed, but for the time being I had to wait for the knowing and the visions that were sure to come to make sense of this grief and all that had happened.

Two days from the place of war, on my brother's land, I spotted a small hill overlooking a beautiful river. It was such a peaceful place, I decided to lay Kingfisher's body to rest there. All the braves waited for me to do the burial ceremony. I asked them to travel on to Chota leaving me a small party of braves to guide me home safely but they refused.

Runner returned from Chota the night before with more braves from our many clans. They too refused to return ahead of us. All I wanted was to be left alone to grieve for my husband, but they were stubborn as expected. They all stayed except Runner, who returned to Chota to retell the story of the Battle of Taliwa.

On the third day after the battle we headed back on the trail towards Chota. We were a day's travel from home. I needed to settle my soul on this last day of this sad lonely trail. I expected that the chiefs would have many questions that I would not want to answer. I prayed the Creator who guides my spirit would give me the proper words to give to them.

By now, Runner had surely reached Chota and retold the stories of the Battle of Taliwa. Until he had returned to gather another war party, my mother had not known where I had gone. Tame Doe's fear for her family was great; now that her daughter, son, and son-in-law were battling the war it increased even more.

The stories of our battles and losses were already being told throughout all Nations. Families were making plans for the grieving ceremonies. My Mother's grief would be different now for this war had taken not only a family member, but also the heart of her daughter.

Heavy with grief, my heart felt as though it could stop beating at any moment. How could I go on without my husband? Many women have felt this loss throughout time, but now I suffered as they. My once vivid dreams and visions suddenly turned to blackness. Have the visions left me for the rest of my life? My mind spun in circles all day. The thoughts were there, but I could not grab them from the spinning in my mind to make sense of them. My people spoke, but I did not hear; their words did not make sense. How long could I go on like this before my mind completely abandoned me?

Seeing Little Kati growing before my eyes was the only pleasure left to me. I was thankful that her unborn sibling would be a beautiful reminder of my warrior now gone. She seemed to understand my need by staying near my side at all times. Was she fearful that I will leave, walk into the hills, and fade away forever to walk among the spirits of the other world? A world, because of my gift – or curse - only I could see. The place I longed to live but could not. Even though I wished to walk among them, they were not ready for me.

My world collapsed again when the flow of blood came at the same time I always received it. Now I grieved for the loss of both my husband and his unborn offspring. Why couldn't this child have stayed with me, a gift of life to help us through? A warrior's son would have carried the spirit of his father forward into time.

Have the spirits abandoned me forever? They did not speak to me any longer. Many times I wished that they would leave me to this world, but now I find that I miss them. The Great Spirit knows best and I would wait for Him to speak to my heart again. For now it was now so full of pain that I could not hear.

Only Little Kati brought me happiness. I saw Kingfisher in her eyes and his expressions crossed her face. Without her, I surely would have walked into the mountains and be gone forever, for my heart and mind cried mournfully and sleep only brought blackness.

The Medicine Man tried many times to return my spirit to me but I would not receive it. The gifts of land and slaves given to me could not heal my pain, for it goes too deep. Would this last forever? My mind could see no end to this pain.

The day that Kingfisher left this world was the saddest day of my life. This day of his burial would also be a day of brutal sadness. To speak of my beloved husband on the hill where we placed him would be the last time for 12 full moons that his name could be spoken aloud amongst the Wolf Clan. My name,

Nanyehi, means one who walks among the spirits. Now I feel I am walking the land alone. I feel nothing but pain. How could I make my spirit want to live again? My child would need me, as would my people. I felt abandoned even though I knew the Creator still watched over my heart. Even still, to remove my right arm would be less painful.

The warriors all remained and we performed the burial ceremony as I laid my warrior to rest. I placed inside all that was his. Every warrior paid honor to him by placing one of their belongings with this body. These warriors left behind valued weapons in respect for his warring way. I did not want to leave that spot on the hill where I was leaving my heart as well. The travel back to Chota I do not remember, so lost in my mind that as I entered the town I did not notice all the clan that came to welcome our return.

The tears in my family's eyes were not hidden. This day we grieved as one family. When we arrive at my longhouse, the people were all gathered around.

Chiefs Attakullakulla and Oconostoa walked to my door at the longhouse, accompanied by my mother and Little Kati. The sadness on their faces made my heart hurt all the more, my head grew light and my knees weakened. I knew not how to stand tall as the home we shared and our possessions had left this world to go to the next where Kingfisher awaited.

With my closest family by my side, I took the torch from the man I looked to as my father, Attakullakula, my brother, The Raven, and my cousin, Dragging Canoe. They walked me to our longhouse, the storage house and the winter house that were all now to be burned. I laid the torch against our houses and all watched in silence as the homes I had shared with my husband burned with great flames, the smoke rising toward the sky. All our things left me in the flames.

I heard him whispering to me through the smoke of time, "I will be by your right side always, Skinny Woman." One day my Kingfisher and I would be as one again.

The town's voice rose in a deep chant as the homes of our families burned down to the ground, as Mother Earth received the ashes. My loss was not the only one; he was deeply loved by his People. As the time of mourning tore through my soul, I grieved with the same passion of when I once loved him. Mother, Little Kati, and I all grieved as one, so great the pain of our loss.

Exhaustion overtook me and when I could grieve no longer we arose from hours of great wailing and sorrow. As I looked around my eyes could not believe the sight. My family replaced all the things that I had just lost …and more in only a day. After the passing of a loved one, the custom of the Cherokee people is to burn the longhouse where they lived as well as their belongings, sending them to the other world where their spirit dwells. After the ritual, all things sent with Kingfisher into his new life were replaced by the people of Chota. Our Long House and winter home and all that filled them were replaced before the moon came on the day we returned to Chota. I had never seen all of one's processions replaced so quickly. The honor was great but it did not lift my spirits.

The day had worn into two and my body screamed for the blackness that could only be brought by sleep. The kindness of my people would ensure we had soft mats inside our new longhouse.

I heard a clamor amongst all the family that still gathered at my home. They parted and allowed the Chiefs, who were in full dress, to pass through our people. The confusion in my head was great and I knew not what to make of the formal ceremony that was about to take place.

My uncles stepped forth holding the great wings of an Eagle. Could this be happening to me? I grew weaker once more. I had heard stories by the fires as the ancient ones described what I was now seeing, this honor plays before me.

Chief Attakullakulla spoke:

"Our most beloved daughter of the Cherokee has shown much bravery during the Battle of Taliwa, as our braves began their retreat. During this battle, Nanyehi raised her weapon and charged forward with the cry of battle and led our people as the fiercest warrior Chief among the Cherokee. All are gathered here to witness your rise to Chieftainess.

From this time forth you will sit amongst the Chiefs of the Council House. Your word will be law among our people. The wisdom and bravery you have shown will be remembered by the fires for all time. Without your bravery I know the loss to our tribe would have been much greater."

The voice of my family chanting in harmony sounded throughout the town of Chota, and for this moment in time they sang as one. This lifted my spirits and I felt blood again flowing in my veins.

After the people quieted, Chief Oconostoa began to speak. "The name we have bestowed upon our daughter will be "Ghi gh u", Beloved Woman of the Cherokee." Both of my uncles walked toward me and embraced me. They placed white feathered wings upon my shoulders.

The time passed strangely, it was as if another person was inside of me. This odd feeling lasted until my mother and daughter walked on my left side to our new longhouse. There, in our new longhouse, I fell into a long, dark sleep.

Although a great honor had just been bestowed upon me, I could not shake my pain. Grief took me to a place where all was black and white. No color could I see. I did not want to live another day in this world without Kingfisher. I was forbidden by law to speak aloud the name of the person I loved most for 12 full moons. His name was not to cross my lips, even in a whisper. This was the Cherokee tradition that had to be upheld. How was I going to be able to do this, where would I to get the strength to go on?

For many days, I did not leave my bed and could not eat or drink much. I begged the Creator for the silence of sleep. When I did sleep it was fitful. My dreams were filled with fights, and seeing again and again the loss of my beloved husband. I cried out for him in these dreams, asking him to take me with him. Each time I awoke, I was in the same place I went to sleep. On a mat he had never slept upon. With our possessions now burned into the smoke of time, I'm saddened that I cannot reach them, touch them, or smell of him. The fight in my heart and mind wore on through many days and all I wanted to do was sleep and hoped that death would take me.

One morning before the dawn came, I awoke with an urge to return to the place I was most happy. I left the longhouse and took the trail that would return me to the place of our first coupling, this place that he had made for us that would always be ours.

It seemed to take weeks to return to the place where we shared our love. It was there I would go to forever be with him, in the land where he now dwelled. Upon my arrival at the place that he had fashioned, I looked everywhere for him, hoping that somehow he would come back to me here.

I could hear his voice telling me, "If we are ever separated, this is where we will come." He must still be here somewhere, for I feel him so strongly. I went to the falls thinking he might be there but returned alone to our nest to wait for him. He would come soon and take me with him, I was sure.

In my grief and confusion, I became ill and tired. I lay down for what would surely be the last time until I awoke with the love of my life. When next I awoke, it was not my husband's eyes that were staring into mine. They were the eyes of the White Wolf staring deep into mine, my Spirit Walker. I had no fear of the White Wolf as he passed the knowledge he had for me into my mind. His message was this: the one I sought was not here. I needed to return home and prepare my people for the future. A future forever altered, should I not live on. Spirit Walker had brought fresh kill for me to eat. My husband had left our small longhouse well stocked of wood and pots to cook with. The kill was fresh and limp with death. I asked the brother rabbit to bless me before I dressed him to cook. I drank his blood and ate his heart and felt the strength swiftly return back to me.

I went to the stream to drink, then returned to our special place, and slept until dawn. Again, I ate and drank. When my strength and right mind returned, I then left for Chota.

The pony I had ridden stayed with me through these many days. Our ponies are trained to return home if they were left un-tethered. This special pony, however, knew my need and had stayed with me.

Many times on the journey home I would hear the Spirit Wolf whispering in my ears, urging me on towards home. He told me when to rest and when to go on. By the end of the second day, my strength subsided and I fell to the ground from my pony. Tired, thirsty, and hungry, I went fast into a deep sleep. Our ponies are taught to be still when their rider has fallen and to stay in place so as to not harm their rider. When I awoke, it was to the sounds of my restless ride.

The leaves around me moved ever so slightly. The hair on my arms arose so I lay as still as possible. The next thing I heard was the voice of my brother, The Raven. My brother gathered me in his arms and rocked me slowly as I cried a thousand tears over the loss of my beloved. He knew how much I had loved my husband and he cried with me there.

After I was fed and had my fill of water we traveled towards home. When we arrived, my mother thanked the Creator for once again bringing her daughter home. Tame Doe cared for me as she feared for my life in this world for she knew I had not wished to stay here without my husband.

By the second full moon of the loss of my beloved, my belly started to roll, a sickness came upon me and all I could do was sip the water from the mystic spring that Tame Doe and Little Kati brought to me. The Medicine Man came to our new longhouse each morning with the dawn and with each setting sun. He brought many potions and herbs that did nothing to make me well. Many times I felt that I would enter the other world. The Great Spirits were still not speaking to me. The visions were dead to me.

Noises woke me on the night after the moon was full. I struggled to go outside of the longhouse. I crawled across the floor of our longhouse making sure that Tame Doe and Little Kati were safe from what was sure to be approaching our home.

As I crawled from the longhouse, my eyes were drawn to the spot by the river where I first saw Kingfisher. This spot was lit with a soft glow. I struggled to my feet, where I found the strength to stand could only have been sent by the Great Spirit for I had not eaten well in days and I yearned only for the water of the Mystic Spring. The soft glow stayed and I made my way toward it. There was movement, but I was not frightened. I slowly made my way to the bank of the river. Was I dreaming again?

Before me sat Kingfisher with the soft ambers of a small fire that lit the features of the man I knew so well. He arose and took my hand. "Beloved," he said, "For much time I have waited here for you." I went to him and fell into his waiting arms. Words would not leave my mouth, so I drew strength from his strong arms that wrapped tightly around me. The energy from his spirit body pulsed through mine making me stronger with each passing beat of my heart.

Kingfisher whispered, "My heart once beat for you in our world and still beats for you in my new world. The People have need of you, sister, you must return to them. Our Little Kati and our unborn son need you to teach them the way of our People so our seeds will last until the end of time. Much is the work you have left to do," he stated. "My Beloved I am with you always. I am on your right side for all time in both worlds."

The soft whispers of Kingfisher gave the knowing that I needed to go on. I began to feel life inside me; the unborn child I thought I had lost was moving. The visions returned. I saw our son grow into a great warrior. I saw our little Kati fully grown, holding hands with her many children and the spirits of her future seeds around us.

Kingfisher held me through the night. The fire he built for us stayed strong and warm and he did not let me go. I could see smoke rising from the Smoking Mountains, more than ever before. The spirits of the mountains were all at work blessing this day and the return of my warrior to my arms.

"Beloved, know I am with you always in the trees, the rivers, the air that you breath, I am in all things, most of all, I am in you," he said softly. He placed his hand where my heart was now beating strongly. I fell asleep in his arms, in the mist of the early morning.

I awoke to a gentle nudging as the sun shone brightly through the slits of my eyes. Little Kati's face was all I could see and the love in her eyes was that of her father. Tears welled in my eyes.

"Mother," she said. "I woke and you were not there so I came to find you. The fire you built is dying, you should come home now. Grandmother would be worried about us if she wakes and we are not there. Mother, the light is in your eyes and the color of the wild rose once again is in your cheeks." At this, Little Kati touched her mother's cheek and a small smile crossed her little face.

"Of course it has, I replied. Your father is once again with us." I looked over and he was not there! My heart jumped and sank again. "Yes, mother," she said softly, "he is always with us." She placed one hand on her heart and said, "He will always be here."

I took her into my arms and as I did, behind her on the bank of the river, I saw the White Wolf standing guard. As the sun rose higher, he walked toward the edge of the woods and disappeared.

Again, I felt the morning sun on my face, my heart had the beat of a new song and rhythm, the earth smelled new and I truly felt my daughter's arms around me. I thought with such a clearness I had not felt for many moons. My beloved Kingfisher walked the bridge that connects our worlds and showed me a path I could take through what was left of my life.

The wee one in my stomach flittered with life, a seed that was growing inside me, a seed filled with the love of his parents brought anew in the darkness of night. I knew he was safe and would grow and live to be strong. I knew the dreams were back, but this night and dawn were not a dream, it was as real as holding Kati in my arms.

We arose and headed back to our longhouse. When we entered, Tame Doe was busy with the preparing of the morning meal. "I heard him call to you in the night my daughter, you are back from your sadness, are you not?" she asked.

I blushed and said, "It is true, he came to me on the rush of a wind and bade me to him by the river where I first saw him. We talked the night through and I fell asleep in his arms. When I awoke, Little Kati was there to fill my arms and in six moons there will be a son to also fill my arms and days. The ways of the ancients I will teach him and he will grow into a great warrior chief like his father," I paused and spoke his name one last time, "Kingfisher."

Tame Doe said, "My prayers are answered; you have come back to us, daughter. Your people are in great need of you, and your wisdom." A single tear trailed down my mother's cheek.

I stated, "All is back my mother. These many days I have been lost in my mind, the screaming of my soul echoes off my heart where it once lay dead. I was choking with my own grief, not able to see anyone else's. Forgive me my mother; I have let you all down because of my grief."

Tame Doe said, "my daughter, you have not let the People down, you have been tired and full of sorrow. A part of you died on the battlefield with Kingfisher and I knew when you found yourself again, you would come back to us. You are now *Ghighau*. The name suits what you have become "Beloved Woman" of our People. The pride I feel to be your mother has always filled me with such joy, my child. Know that since your tenth year you have been the "Beloved of the People." She straightened her body as she said these things. Tame Doe, being the daughter of a great chief, learned young and stayed strong in

113

her belief and in the ways of our people. She had taught my brother and I well. Her wisdom teaches Little Kati and would soon teach my son the ways of the ancient ones.

Ghighau

The slave of the Shawnee warrior, who knocked me to the ground with a war club at the Battle of Taliwa, came to me with a branch of white pine bough as a symbol of peace between him and me. They had been living amongst the Creek and French soldiers for many seasons. Though many of our tribes have taken slaves, there were none in our lodges. To send his slave away would bring upon both of their dishonor, so we welcomed her as a new daughter in the home of my mother.

After the battle of Taliwa, the Creek and their allies moved from the lands around Ball Ground abandoning the edge of our hunting grounds. They left our lands in a great hurry, but as they did so, they did not even leave their warriors who had fought bravely that day. The same as we, they took their dead from that place.

The following weeks passed slowly. The loss of many men from Chota was felt deeply by all. Our ways made sure we did not show our grief after the long days of wailing. I now see how hard our ways are. Many are the times that I would walk far from our home, sit alone with myself, pray, and allow the tears to flow from my eyes. Little Kati missed her father, but she was still young and it would soon seem as only a dream to her.

My dreams are filled with my husband still. Now, though, they are not all of the day he was killed. Some are of happy, simple times and some are of him holding me and whispering sweet words of love in my ear. They can seem so real it makes me think he has returned to me from the other world. My time of sadness will last a lifetime. Stolen from me are the arms that once held me tightly. We both fought for what we believed in and for the survival and strength of our people.

I can see our lands being taken from us when we have no more to give. Our blood would continue to be spilled upon the land that I love, a land we have fought for and lost so much to. I prayed always for the Creator to continue to show me the way to peace. Peace upon our land and peace for my broken heart.

I continue to pray for a peace I fear will never come in my lifetime. Through my pain, I will do as I must for my people, my children and our grandchildren that will come to be, for they are part of the future I see for this young America. I hold the bump of my stomach that is still hidden from view. The nights are long and filled with memories; this is the last secret Kingfisher and I share.

One afternoon, Runner showed up at our longhouse with a message. We were requested to come to the lodge of Chief Attakullakulla. When we arrived at the longhouse of my Uncle, we were honored with the respect of many chiefs. We were seated across from my Uncle who for much time sat and looked long into my eyes. There are times that there are words that need not be spoken. Our eyes were filled with love for each other, our family, the Wolf Clan, our Kittawa brothers and for the Cherokee Nation. My uncle then spoke, "Ghighau it is an honor to have you at my longhouse. My sister sent word with the rise of the sun that you were well again."

Again, he spoke only more softly, "My sister's daughter is through her time of grief?"

I nodded my answer. He spoke again, "The People will be pleased that you walk among us once more. We have awaited your return as we are in much need of the wisdom of your counsel on many matters, but this can wait for you to get stronger, my daughter."

"Yes uncle," I spoke softly.

"My sister and I have brought forth strong seeds. Our children are led by the Great Spirit. The courage you and your husband showed on that day of his loss will forever be told in the longhouses of our family and by the fires of the Creek. Your children and the children of your cousins will prosper from our blood and from the blood that was shed to protect them from those that would kill us and our seed." Attakullakulla stopped speaking and closed his eyes. "Go rest, Ghighau, Beloved Woman." As I arose to leave, I saw a single tear stain the face of my uncle.

The moon was rising and I saw Old Water's shadow cross my door. There had been much life that had passed since last he had put the marks on my face. We sat and ate by the fire and spoke of what had happened to my husband and the many moons that had followed. We talked of things to come and of things lost. We sat like this most of the night before he fell fast asleep. Old Water's hands were still strong and steady, though he was sad for my losses, he felt proud to place upon my hand and legs the marks he saw for me.

Morning came and after bathing, I returned to the longhouse to talk with Old Water and to eat a meal of warm bread and honey. We seeped a fresh tea of roses, ginseng and catmint. This would help to slow my heart and ward off any pain.

As Ghighau my life would be much harder, for I held the life and death of many in my hands. For as alone as I felt inside, it was soothing to know I was never alone. Mother or little Kati always seemed to be close by my side. Then there were those who sought me for my counsel in their need. This number grew with each passing season.

Old Water told me he had waited for my time of grief to not be so fresh. He had been having dreams that he was storing to know what to paint upon my body. He saw the wheel of life at the center of my hand with the red lines of our people leading to the center of this wheel. This would represent the long lines of our people into the future of the chains of life. The band of the four directions stood for my increased power. All placed upon my left hand, the side of our bodies that speak from a place of peace.

Upon my ankles, Old Water placed the marks of my ruling powers as a war woman. Though I wished not to fight, it was evident I would to the death. The markings placed on my ankles were that of inter mingling lines that encircled completely. In between these inter mingling lines was the mountain like peaks that were bordered in. The final line at the bottom was that of a beaded mark which represented the beads of the earth, the berries that were used by our people for much.

My wounds of battle had healed quickly, it was my heart I was sure would break to the end of my time. My work for the people and the love of my family would have to be enough to keep me from walking into the mountains to die.

As the many suns of the summer season came and went, I took much pleasure in walking the many trails around our village. Happiness returned to my heart at the sight of Little Kati growing as well as the swell of my stomach. As glad as I was that the sickness had not stayed with me through these days, daily I praised my Creator for his kindness, for the passing of my sickness and for the time he granted me with Kingfisher that night on the banks of the Little Tennessee River.

With this new name of Ghighau came new responsibilities. The people came with questions that still needed answered and there were many dreams to interpret. The Cherokee people had to fulfill all of my requests and obey any orders that I give. Such a power had only been known but to a few of our nation. My decisions were not to be questioned by either woman or man. With a power such as this, I knew I would have to be very careful in my words, for they would be taken literally and could mean life or death. The Great Spirit would not put upon me more than He could help me bare. My prayer to Him was to keep my mind and heart placed on His will. We as a people make many mistakes but the Creator makes none.

In my twenty second summer, we journeyed to the hunting grounds through the opening at Cumberland and traveled through the secret passage that led to Kentucky and Ohio. There, the hunting grounds were plentiful and there were many sacred places searched out. Magic places, where the stars aligned with the summer and fall harvest moons, were where the ancient mound builders placed drawings upon the ground. These paths lit the way for the giants that had been sent to our lands from places beyond the stars who helped populate the earth.

The gift of the red bird was of great comfort to my soul as we followed the paths of the ancients. I believed my father had sent the red bird from beyond the shadow of time because it guided us on our way. The bird, along with the ancient ground markings, pointed us toward the sacred mounds in the land of Ohio.

After the crops were set out in the early spring, my mother, brother and I set out with a hunting party and made our way through the lands of Kentucky. We heard an odd singing coming through the mountains. Dragging Canoe and Fivekiller set out to track the noise and came upon a Unaka that was large like a giant. He was walking through the mountains alone, singing to the sky. The man was surely touched by the Gods. He should not walk these mountains alone, singing at the top of his voice for all of man to hear. The giant of a man had a wide mouth, his britches and shirt were made from the skins of deer. He also carried skins attached to his pack. This hunter would surely not live for long. As we continued toward the river that would take us to the land of the giants, we once again came across the singing in the mountains. This giant man was also making his way toward what seemed to be the same place as we were going.

We would be hard to detect, as our People have ways of moving and yet not being seen. We blended in amongst the trees, fields and bushes we have grown up amongst. The Cherokee tribe had grown and divided many times, and yet we still continued to grow in numbers. In the time of the ancients, we learned how to survive the cold and great storms of Mother Nature.

Our main purpose for this trip was set under the cloak of a party of hunters. We were destined for the Mount of the Serpent. The Uncles had asked of me to watch the aligning of the stars to the earth. By doing so, I would see the great serpent snake. The ancient Adena tribe built these mounds to guide all that would seek and see the great power of the sky and who dwells there. There are many mounds that were built throughout this region, all built with purpose and plan, and I longed to set foot near them.

These places of wonder were well-guarded, sacred grounds of sanctuary. Tribes from far off places gathered here to trade and celebrate the coming and going of seasons. Blessed are those who seek, for here we find new ways of medicine and together share ceremonies of life continued. There was such beauty in this land, colors so alive and rich with berries and flowers where soon fruit would grow.

The laurels of the mountains were still in bloom, even though our land had seen these colors and blooms two full moons before. The red bird guided my steps and the Creator guided my heart as I entered magic places, knowing he walked with me, sending his gentle giants along the way.

On the sixth full moon of my season with child, Tame Doe came to talk of an important subject. I knew this because I saw Runner go to our longhouse and Kati followed after him as he left. Runner had been assigned a new position since the Great War at Taliwa with the Creek. A position he would hold until he chose not to. He would tell stories by the fire and stay near Attakullakulla, Oconostoa, and me. When my mother returned, I could tell by the look across her face that she had many things to tell me.

"My daughter," she began, "my brother sent for me to speak of a marriage," she hesitated.

"But mother, you are too old to consider such a thing," I giggled.

"Not me, child, you," she said.

"Oh mother, who would want a wife with one child and fat with another?" I asked.

"That is what I asked of my brother, but it is true. The one inquiring is an Irishman who was once a soldier in the British army. He is a trapper that has been watching you, my daughter," she stated proudly.

Still shocked by this proposition, I stated, "I will have to think on this my mother."

Mother replied, "Attakullakulla awaits your answer, he sent Runner to deliver your answer to him". At that Runner entered our longhouse and awaited my orders.

"Runner," I said, "tell our Chief that I first must speak with him and meet this man who asks to become my husband."

At that, he turned and started to run to the longhouse of my uncle. What seemed only moments later, he returned with a message for me to come before the setting of the sun.

I prepared myself to meet with my uncle, Chief Attakullakulla and the stranger who wanted me for his wife. I agreed to meet him only because Attakullakulla asked this of me. My uncle must have his reasons to propose this union so close to the loss of my husband. Had I not had a dream that there would be another child for me, a third seed, I would have resisted this strange request. Cherokee men would not come forward to marry a woman of my stature for the power I held and my standing within the tribe. Cherokee men want to be first in the longhouse of their mate and this could never be for me again. Kingfisher would always rule my heart. As he had said to me before, he would always stand to my right for all of time.

The walk with Runner to the longhouse of Chief Attakullakulla seemed to take much longer than the last time he requested my presence. Again, I was treated as an equal and brought to the fire to sit across from my uncle.

"Ghighau," Attakullakulla spoke strongly, "Have you an answer for me?"

"My uncle," I began, "This man comes not from a tribe."

"Niece, this man is an Irishman, a trapper, who would be honored to take you for his wife. He understands some of our ways and will honor your position here. The People would not want you to leave us to join with the Unaka world," he stated.

"How does he know of me uncle?" I asked.

"This I will let him tell you. He is here and wants me to present him to you." He said and waited for me to speak next.

"Is this as you wish my uncle, for me to marry out of our tribe to a man of another world, a man who traps and kills our brother and sister animals, takes food from our people's bellies, takes from us fur and skins that we need to cloth our children and old ones?" I asked sternly.

"I see this as a union of our peoples. Have you not said we must understand the Unaka and their ways? Would this not give you a greater understanding of their ways so you could teach him and the white man of our ways?" he asked.

"Uncle, I will meet this man you speak of. I have many questions to ask of him," I stated.

Chief Attakullakulla nodded to Runner to bring the Irishman to parlay with us. Then the silence was broken as a large bear of a man entered the longhouse of my Uncle to be presented to me.

"Ghighau, this is Bryant Ward," my uncle stated. At this, Attakullakulla arose from his place by the fire and left the longhouse.

I sat in silence studying this man. Though his hair had grown for many seasons, it did not cover his eyes. The hair on his face was long, but looked soft like the mane of a Cherokee pony. It was his eyes that drew me to him. They were as blue as a summer sky. I waited for him to speak. Mr. Ward knelt beside me and took my hands in his. I held myself like an ironwood tree, strong and unmoving.

"My God, but you are beautiful," he stared kindly as he spoke.

I sat still and did not speak. He dropped my hands from his.

"I am so sorry to have blurted that out, but you are very beautiful. It's true you have the blush of a rose petal to your cheeks, but a rose pales by your beauty. Remarkably, the townsmen spoke the truth of your beauty," he said in a lower voice. "My lady, where are my manners?" he reached for my hand again and bowed his head to it. "My name is Bryant Ward. It is my pleasure to make your acquaintance, ma lady."

All I could do was look at this mountain of a man. As I looked closer, I noticed his kind eyes and slowly a smile began to spread across my face. He still held my hand in his and when I began to stand, he helped me to my feet. Bryant Ward did not know that I understood the language of the English. My uncle had seen to my knowing the English language. He told me long ago that we need to understand the new people and know their talk so that we may be prepared for what comes.

"Mr. Ward, why do you want to marry me?" I asked of him in his language, as I watched an even larger smile spread across his face.

He began by saying, "From the day I saw you stand as a warrior and kill your Creek enemy at the battle of Taliwa, when you raised your weapon screaming out the war cry, I have not been able to remove you from my thoughts. I watched your husband die and have worried since then that you would not make it through the winter without a man in your longhouse. I have learned from your Chief that this is not so. I know now that you are well cared for by your clan, but Nanyehi, I still wish for you to become my wife. Such beauty and bravery I do admire. I had a wonderful wife who died young and a son who is being raised by my family in Ireland. I can see no other as my wife but you," he paused.

As I sat quietly without a word, he continued, "Please, will you do me the honor of becoming my wife?"

I could not help but smile at this large man whose presence was more welcoming than intimidating despite appearances. "I will marry you Mr. Ward, but only in the way of the white man," I boldly stated, expecting him to decline my demand.

"Well, what other way is there?" he belted out with joy in his voice. Mr. Ward took my hands again and said, "You've made me very happy this day."

When this day began I was the widow of a war chief, and before the next moon came full I would be the wife of a white man.

The day had been long so I spent the night in the longhouse of my uncle. Sleep was calling me. Dreams came to me this night, dreams that I would not understand until much later in life. Dreams that I prayed would not come true.

I dreamt I saw my children growing older in the shadows of our beautiful smoking mountain, their lives interrupted by the strange ways of the white men. The vision of my children was of three. Two were of dark skin and one with lighter skin. This Bryant Ward was to be the father of one. I have seen this child in my visions. My hopes are that I would have many children, but I have seen this is not to be. I dreamt of stone lodges reaching into the skies and darkness covering the ground where the grass should grow. In this dream the rivers were full of dead fish lining her banks. I saw my people walking in long lines with tears streaming down their faces.

When I awoke with my clothes and bedding soaked through to the mat from sweat, I wondered who I should tell of these new dreams. For the moment, I felt it was best to hold these dreams to myself.

The lit fire which kept off the chill of morning was dying down. I laid where I had slept while thinking of these dreams. Etching them in my mind, surely the Great Spirit would reveal more to me in the days ahead. I would then know what to do with this knowledge.

The others started to awake around me and we began our day. On the slow walk home, I was again accompanied by Runner. Many of the people stopped me and offered gifts for the child they all knew I now carried. They gave me also food and drink.

These are the days that I treasure, the return of my life and that of the one who grows inside me. Our son would look much like his father, the beautiful man I called my husband.

Little Kati and her namesake were working outside the longhouse when I returned from my night at the longhouse of uncle Attakulakula. I could see the questions in Kati's eyes. I did not want to talk in front of Little Kati. Mother drew up a bowl of food to keep Little Kati busy so we could talk on these matters that happened the night before.

"Did your meeting go well with the Irishman, my daughter?" Kati asked with question in her voice.

"Yes, my mother," I replied, "all went well. "Attakulakula and I talked long into the night," I paused. "Do you know of these things, my mother?"

Kati replied, "My brother told me much, but it is what you have to talk of that has my ear, child."

"I tell you that I will marry Bryant Ward by the next full moon. With much thought I will marry him in the white man's way. His children will be of two worlds and they will need to know both. We will go to Charlestown and marry there in his world but we will live in my world, here in Mother Chota. He knows that I cannot leave our land and that my place is among our people. Do you agree my mother?" I asked her.

Kati began, "As you wish my child. For who am I to tell you of the life you must lead? There is much to be done. When will you leave our Chota to make this trip to Charlestown?"

"Bryant Ward will bring a wagon in three moons. There is much to be done and the burdens that I placed upon us are many, we must begin to make ready my journey," I told her.

The next days were full of plans to enlarge our longhouse as we would soon have two more people to take care of.

As was arranged, Bryant Ward came for me on the fourth rise of the sun and we began our journey to the white man's town to marry in the way of the white man. To my wonder, many in this town seemed to know who I was. I was not unfamiliar with this place as I had taken many journeys into this other world in years past. Many things I saw.

We went to the place where Bryant Ward worshipped his God, and we said the words that joined us to each other in marriage until death. Mr. Ward was very kind to me on our journey. That night we rested at an Inn in town. I took note of the white man's items in this place, noting the sleeping mat had carved posts with a feather filled frame. There was much in this world I had not seen before.

Bryant said, "The preacher changed your name to *Nancy*, for he could not discern the spelling of your names. Is this pleasing to you, my lass, for it would also be less of a challenge for me?"

I thought for a few moments and said, "Mr. Ward, if that would make you happy, I will answer when you address me as such. This will be my new, white man's name, Nancy Ward."

"Yes that sounds right. Now rest, my wife, I can see the tiredness in your eyes," he said and turned to leave the room we shared. He was right, tired I was.

Nancy

The next rising of the sun awoke me from my sleep. Mr. Ward was sleeping in a chair by the sleeping mat where food and water were by his side. I had slept dreamless for many hours.

Mr. Ward stirred from his slumber and this large man, my new husband, came to life before my eyes. He had a gentle smile for me and spoke, "When I left you last night to get you supper, I was waylaid by the innkeeper. Seems I have indeed married well. Your name carries before you, my new wife. This will indeed be a prosperous union. The fur traders will come to me now that I have a permanent interest in this land."

Mr. Ward must have seen the concern in my eyes for he dropped his head and put his hands together and looked up at me and said, "Tis not the reason I asked you to be my wife, but now there will be many in my family. I know some of your Cherokee customs. I know I am to join your clan and live in your longhouses. I will rely on you to teach me all I must know to fit into your world," he said.

I could not help but grin as his words were kind and by his face I could tell that he meant what he said. "Yes, Mr. Ward," I began, and he stopped me with his raised hand.

"Pardon ma'am," he said. "We are now married, would you please call me by my first name? Mr. Ward is too proper."

"Bryant, happy I will be to teach you the ways of the Cherokee. We will have much time to do as you've asked." I was uneasy to tell him my next thoughts, as he seemed so kind and genuinely caring. He had been thoughtful to bring me food and water, and even though I slept he did not awaken me. I was worried that my new husband would call upon me to sleep with him in the darkness of night, and yet he simply slept in his chair. I began my thoughts slowly, to see how he would react to my next words. "So kind you were not to wake me during the night."

"Ah ma'am, uh Nancy, 'twas asleep you were and pardon me, but I am a gentleman behind this wooly beard. You have need of your rest and the child that you carry is important to you and your people. We will soon have our time. You see, Nancy, I want you to love me first," he paused, "and we will know when or if you will love me."

The next morning we arose before the dawn and left Charlestown and returned to Chota. The journey was eased by the fact that we now had a horse and buggy and he brought his servants with us. This practice of having servants and slaves was not a new one to me, for I had freed any slaves that were given to me. We were bound by treaty with the white man to return all slaves to their rightful owners. Some were returned and other were adopted into our tribe. I would, however, do my best to respect the ways of my husband as I hoped he would also respect mine.

When we entered Chota, the people greeted us with kindness and the longhouse had been enlarged by my people so it was ready for my new husband and his servant's arrival. It was stocked with the things we would need, my people were truly kind. Long ago, we had learned to help each other. We are all family and with this we are charged with the tending of each other's needs. The Great Spirit long ago showed our people the way and we practiced what the Ancient ones taught us since the beginning of time.

As the next two full moons passed, I grew very large with Kingfisher's child. Time was spent doing things I had always done, though it was slower. I was happy the time would soon come that my son would come from his warm, watery sleep and dwell beside me in our longhouse. I was seeing into the future these months and still felt I should keep my visions and dreams to myself. Of the many questions that would surely come, I had no answers. I would wait for the Creator to show me whom and when to speak of these things.

Bryant was learning the customs of our people and he was accepting of many of our ways. He also taught me of his ways during these many moons since he had come to live in our longhouse. The Cherokee came to learn many new practices from Bryant. We are quick to learn the ways of others. This is how we have been able to stay strong and alive and live with the Unaka for as long as we have.

Bryant fashioned from wood a canoe that rocked for the baby to sleep in. He told me of his wife of long ago and I told him more of Kingfisher. Odd were many of his ways. He came to me one day excited as he handed me many flowers he had harvested. I came to understand he thought of these flowers as a gift. This gesture I grew to like very much. My new husband was taking a place in my heart and my new life was bringing new joy.

As my time of birthing approached, Ward - the name by which I now called him - began to stay closer to the longhouse and again I found myself pleased that he thought of us as his family. He took many chores from Kati and me without the mention of even a word. He fit into the clan well, despite his full beard and tall stature. I was pleased with this new husband of mine, but never lost love for Kingfisher as the birth of his and my son drew near.

My brother Longfellow and his wife came to visit our mother Kati. They were now living to the south in the towns they created for themselves in the Overhill country. Some of our clan preferred to live this way, a way of separation. Being part of a large clan can present problems for some.

We were glad that Longfellow and his wife were among us for the Corn celebration, a time for feasting, gaming and fellowship with the Great Spirit. The Great Spirit and our Earth Mother had been good to us and the winter storehouses were full. They had followed the eternal flame which was brought to us from Red Clay to our Mother Chota for the relighting of our fires. It is tradition to relight our fires anew each year where the flame must always remain.

As my birthing time drew near, my dreams began to reveal more to me and some of these dreams were already coming to pass. Still though, I had no understanding of many of them. One evening, I sat talking with my mother and as easily as I could, I began to tell her of the dreams and visions that were coming to me.

"It is wise that you have kept these things to yourself, daughter. I fear that our people will not have understanding of these things and I am glad that you have told them only to me. I do not have your wisdom, but I do see why you have chosen to tell me. Fear not, you are *Ghighau* and the Great Spirit has favored you all of your life. They will also favor this child that your carry and the seed of your first husband will live on with you forever. Ward has been helpful and tender to you and little

Kati and has taken on many things that I used to do. He will care also for your new child. He is a good Unaka."

"Mother, it is my hope Ward will be able to help other Unaka understand our ways. Some of their beliefs are like ours. Even Attakullakulla has sought Ward's advice. More of the Cherokee people are accepting this man I have married," I said proudly.

After we retired for the night, the signs began to come. Kingfisher's son was ready to enter the world. Ward awoke and saw that I was in the labors of childbirth and rose to awaken Kati who quietly readied the birthing area. This child was coming much quicker than his sister did and by sunrise, I was holding my beautiful son in my arms.

Ward was glad to meet my son. His first words to him were, "Hello Little Fellow." Thus he got his name. I knew mother would be happy at this as well as my brother. The Raven, who was also known as Longfellow, had stayed on after the Corn ceremony and was glad that he did. The similarity of his name and his new nephew's name made him proud. He and Ward were becoming true brothers and for this I was happy.

Many nights Kingfisher came to me in my dreams as I slept in the smoke of time. He was as I always remembered him. Kind, loving, and the most beautiful man I've ever seen. He showed me how much the love we shared meant to him. I saw in his eyes that he would always be with me. When I awake, I feel as though he has just left to go hunting or off to war. I know not how or why he comes most nights.

Ward's patience was incredible. He was content to teach me more of the white man's ways as well as to teach me how to read and write their words. One day I knew the language of the

Cherokee would be written onto the talking leaves of the Unaka, for I had seen it in a vision.

Ward was a good provider for my family and taught all of us many good ways. He could not replace the love of my life, but his place was secure. His mat in our longhouse would stay until he goes to live with the spirits that have passed from us. In this place Kingfisher would thank Ward and embrace him for the love and kindness he gave to me and our children.

Kati was in her eighth set of seasons, and wise beyond her years. My son, Little Fellow, had seen three full seasons when I realized that Ward needed me to fully become his wife. All this time I had remained faithful to Kingfisher, but my new husband deserved to become one with me as I put the past behind. Plus, I had come to desire him in the ways of man and woman. Ward had waited a long time to lay with me and has been faithful only to me. My love for him grew much these many seasons. When he returned from this hunt, I decided, I would finally give myself to him fully.

Chota was thriving and our wars had been few. The many moons we fought with the Creek seemed to keep them more to their own lands instead of trying to take ours. This would not last long, I was sure, but was glad for this peaceful time with my children.

The Spirits were shining brightly upon my family. The seeds of many Cherokee had been born to this world as I saw visions of many walking far into the future of this land now called America. One day the blood of our people would be mixed with the blood of many that dwelt upon this land. I could not understand all I saw, but I knew that the seeds that were planted would grow for hundreds of years. For I have seen many of my granddaughters in the smoke of time that are yet to be. These visions and dreams of my children assure me that they will grow and prosper along with this country that is becoming full with people from many lands of this earth.

I told the chiefs that we must not sell or trade our lands any longer so we can slow down what I have seen in the smoke of time. The scattering of our people is what I was trying to stop, but I knew already this could not be so.

Upon Ward's return from his fur trading, I felt a love rise up that I only recognized from my warrior. Many nights I had fallen asleep in this man's arms who loved and protected my family. I felt safe with Ward now. I had prepared much food and water to last three suns. The love Ward would know at the end of these days he had long waited for. Ward then entered our longhouse. I went to him and he knew that the time had come for us to lie down as one. I bathed him and oiled both his body and mine. I had smudged the room with many scents that now filled the air and aroused our senses. The days were still long but I wanted him to know my body, as I longed to know his.

In these days, we made love that was filled with laughter, talking, and much oneness. Ward was filled with love for me and was glad to share his seed that he had saved for this time of our uniting. I thanked the Great Spirit for sending me a man that was willing to wait for my readiness. From this time on, he knew that at any time he asked to lay with me, I would gladly give myself to him.

"Nancy," Ward said, "I have waited a long time for these days with you and I say to you it was well worth the wait, though I had hoped for this much sooner." He brought me to him and we made love again. This man knew how to please a woman. I liked all that he taught me in our days together, my body craved him all the more and my mind melted in happiness each time we came together. The love was different from what I shared with Kingfisher, but through the smoke of time I came to love this man very much.

By the third sun, I was sure that I would bear him a daughter and we would share many years of happiness. My body was happy once more with the knowledge of his love.

Ward knew of my gifts from the Great Spirit, but I felt he would not understand if I told him the things that our future would bring. I told him not of our daughter that was to be, or of the many things I saw coming. I would have to be content for now, to only talk with my mother of these things.

Ward and I had lain together many times. He saw the changes that had begun in my body. After three full moons from our first coupling he asked me if I was with child. "Yes Ward, your seed grows here," as I placed his hand upon my belly. "Our love grows within me," I said. The joy he felt was evident upon his face. He lifted me and we spun in circles laughing and crying.

"Nancy, you have made me so happy. I so miss my son in Ireland and knowing you will give me another child to love makes me a happy man." said Ward.

Ward spoiled us all so much and I was sure it would continue through the arrival of our first child - one of many I hoped. Our marriage did not start from love, but I was sure that it would always be of love now that we were finally together in every way.

The many moons ahead would be filled with many wonderful days teaching the children of our clan, as well as my own children, the ways of our People. The Corn Ceremony was coming soon and the fall harvest would keep all busy again. This year Mother Earth had been very good to us. We had even built extra storage for the abundance of food given by the Great Spirit.

Tame Doe was worrying me this season, for she seemed to not be herself. It is hard to see the person you loved the longest become one of the Ancients. She still did her many chores, but as the cold season came, she started moving even slower. The next time the Medicine Man came to the village, I planned to speak of extra herbs that could help restore her strength. She saw me watching her more and she didn't like me to make over her so I tried to watch when she could not see me.

"Daughter," my mother began, "Please do not watch me so, I have seen many seasons and the work has been hard. I'm happiest when I can still be of use. To watch you grow with child again makes me even happier. Ward has been good to us all and this love you have for him pleases me so. Take good care of him always for he is a man of many uses." She giggled and said, "the smile he wears stays long on his face."

"Mother, I will take good care of him, fear not of this. He is a good man indeed," as I smiled softly.

"What does 'indeed' mean?" Tame Doe asked.

"True," I answered.

"Ah yes, true indeed," she said laughingly.

The mornings passed through the fall and into a mild winter season. The Oaks held their leaves and nuts long into the fall and the bellies of the hawks turned whiter with each day. This told me the deep winter moons would hold much snow. During these months, I was glad for the company of my family that was close by. We played games, laughed, and told many stories. Ward told the children funny stories and taught them new games to play. Kati was nine full seasons now and Little Fellow was almost four. Come spring they would have a new sister to play with and help raise.

These were simple times, peaceful, and bountiful. The game replenished itself and the town of Chota was growing with each new season. Many children were sent to our village from other clans when a sickness spread through their towns. These sicknesses took many parents to the other world, leaving their children to us for raising. I was sad for these children and did all I could to help them find a mother and father to care for them. Chota was not only the capitol of the Cherokee Nation, but also long known as a city of refuge.

My heart sang with new life inside me and Ward was so happy he was hard to keep quiet. Such joy it brought to me to see him this way. Tame Doe seemed to sleep longer and I do worry about her, but she is happy.

Just as I had seen in the signs of the leaves and animals, the snow came hard. The land was covered by as much snow as I could ever remember and travel came to a halt. This last snow trapped many Unaka on the paths and trails around Chota. They were forced to come into our village to survive. We took in many families that winter who were not wise enough to stay away from the Smoking Mountains during the winter months.

Our stored food was still plentiful and I hoped that the kindness shown by our people to these strangers would spread the word that we were not savages or the heathens. We tried as a People to accept what we did not understand, and I could only hope that one day these people would accept us and our ways. We are the original people of this land and yet they did not try to understand our ways. They only wanted to change us, take our land, and kill anyone who tried to stop them. They killed many of the other tribes from the northeast territories and wiped out whole tribes from the face of Mother Earth. The Great Spirit must be very sad at this for we are all His people, even the white Unaka. Would they ever understand this?

With the spring came our daughter: a sweet, happy child. Skin more like her father's than mine, but such a beauty. Her sweetness would take her far in this life. It was too soon to see if she had the knowing, but for her sake I hoped she did not for it is hard seeing and knowing. This, the daughter of Bryant and Nancy Ward, we named Elizabeth, but call Bess.

Our chiefs are old now and the young ones want to prepare to take their place. I am much afraid for the passing of our chiefs as the ancients know best for our people. Attakullakulla has negotiated much with the white man: officers of the British, French, and the New Americans that want to take away the rule of the father from across the sea. We could not trust any of these people. The British tried to keep their word, but with their King father being so far away, it is hard to follow his rule.

One day I knew all of their treachery would be shown. We were not safe in a white man's world. They would not rest until they had taken all from us. My greatest fear was for the People. We must survive at all costs, even if I am to be called a traitor among my own People. Our blood must continue to flow far into the future for this land that we love and would die for. Die we will, for I had seen into the smoke of time that it will be so.

For now, I was content to collect the herbs, flowers, and berries that healed my people and others. The Unaka have bettered their lives by accepting some of our ways. I could not focus on the future, but on living fully in each day the Creator gives.

They called our mountains "The Great Smokies." They named our lands Tennessee, Kentucky, and Ohio. Many of our old towns and villages were taken over by the Unaka who killed us for the sake of land. Though the white man would try to wipe our tribe from the earth and forbid the speaking of the tongue of my people, I have seen our language spoken into the smoke of time.

Dragging Canoe moved to the Overhill and started his own villages. He was anxious to become a Principal Chief to our people but his father, Chief Attakullakulla, was afraid that his son would cause our people much loss of life. Dragging Canoe had the way of the Kittawa, the way to war.

The lives of our chiefs were flickering with the smoke of time and I dreaded the loss of our leaders. These brothers, chiefs Attakulakula and Oconostota, would both leave this world close together to walk with the Great Spirit. This I had seen in my sleep dreams and my awakened dreams. The visions that were to be fulfilled were many and I would miss this time of peace. It would be the last time of peace that my people would ever know. My heart broke for I did all that I could do to hold these times back. The Great Spirit showed me the future of this America and that our People will survive far into the smoke of time. My grandchildren are to walk these lands as long as the Great Spirit blesses them.

Ward calls this Great Spirit God. I like this word, but we have called Him the Great Spirit for as long as our People have been here. Maybe the Unaka would like us better if we were to call Him such?

There were many Christians that traveled throughout towns and villages. They performed acts of what they call conversion to Christianity. They believed we were easily swayed to follow their faith. Because of their zealous way, they could not see that our way was as theirs. They are so blind to this similarity that the Unaka even take credit for our souls won over to their God.

Many times in these moons, I had seen our people sad and beaten, walking trails and lands I do not know. They have tears falling down their faces. This dream always sickens me and I fear this time is growing closer. It is revealed to me more and more what will be. We must survive.

The love I have for my people could not compare to the love I had for my children. It was my seed that I saw in the dreams of the future. My grandchildren would be many, this I know. Of any of my children, I did fear most for my son. He had the beauty of his father and already the young females hurried to fill his needs. He had a way with people and I knew he would one day be a chief, a skilled protector of the Cherokee. There was tired land that surrounded the lodges of our People, a thirsting soil that would be hard to work. His wisdom will help our people survive in the strange places that I see.

Some of our People began in these days to weave the clothing of the Unaka. The clothes they make are pretty with their shiny buttons and lace. I have worn some of these clothes, for when I go to the fort with Ward, I try to blend in better amongst his friends. I find them odd, but I wanted to please Ward.

The happiest times for me were still spent at the stream in the morning. This morning ceremony was a most calming tradition, which I will always need in order to stay strong in my beliefs and the ways for my people. Our belief in clans is what keeps our blood strong. Without this custom, we would wipe ourselves out.

The town people called me Nancy Ward, not my tribe name "Ghighau." I have had many names of honor, but now only in my dreams am I called the name that Kingfisher sang in my ear, "Naneyhi."

I was once given a cow by a woman I saved from certain death, Lydia Bean. I thought it was a small buffalo, but it was not. When a cow is bred with the bull they have a small calf. The mother cow gives much milk, enough to be shared with many. This is the best of the white world. They fed our children with the milk like that of a mother. As hard as the whites want us to be gone, this animal would help give our children a strong start in life and provide food when a mother could not, as well as much usefulness in our cook pots. This has brought about many changes in our way of life and I see not all the ways of the Unaka are terrible ways.

My cousins among the other clans were making trouble for the Cherokee, for they wanted to become even with the Unaka. This way of thinking could not continue. The Unaka would always want to kill for vengeance, and I knew it could never be even.

The fruit and flowers were heavy that spring, showing a fast cold winter ahead. When the flowers took branches to the ground with their weight, the winter ahead would be fierce. This one could be the worst I had ever seen.

Our little Bess was growing quickly. Tame Doe was so very happy when she held our little one, but I saw her light fading and I feared I would lose her, so I let her have charge of my Bess most of the day. She had much to tell our little ones before her light went away.

The summer was good, our game was plentiful, and the fruit was abundant. Our crops were thicker than I could ever remember. The thought of this put a fear in me and I was certain that I would lose Tame Doe before the coldest moons came.

I cried for my Peoples' pain that was to come, but passing along the stories would help us survive long into the future. People listened to the ways of the Ancients, for in the telling is knowledge of how to survive the worst of times and not repeat the sins of the old ones. We sat long by the fires and mother told me all that she could remember of the Clans long ago. There was much to learn of the future by knowing the past. The storms of the future blast in my ears. The only calm for my soul was that the Great Spirit had shown me my grandchildren. The knowing showed me that one of mine would find a way to bring us all together again. I knew my children of the future heard my voice in the smoke of time. We must unite to save our world, a world we all share.

As winter came upon us early, I watched as my mother came to the end of her seasons. Each day I saw less of the light in her eyes. While all was quiet one night, I arose to tend to her last needs. My honor it was to have her ready in the early still of the morning. As her grandmother and my grandmother had given us our first baths, I gave her the last bath of her journey. What a beautiful moment in time it is to ready your parent for the journey into another lifetime. Gathering the possessions that she would need in her next life, and preparing her for that last journey was a great honor.

As the family awoke, one by one we gathered to sit around Tame Doe. Even in her sleep, she was beautiful to me. My soul wept for the company that I was losing, but my heart was excited for the journey she was now on. The Great Spirit taught us to be joyful at the passing of an ancient one for they have the smoke of time with them and we needed to celebrate this. When a loved one is taken early it is harder to accept but we are only allowed a short time to mourn their loss. Time is short and to survive season to season is what is important.

Watching my mother pass from this earth into her next journey brought back the memory of the loss of my first love, Kingfisher. It was the hardest I had ever fallen; tis hard to lose the love of your soul. It was still fresh in my mind the way that I felt, lost and abandoned for what seemed all time. He still ruled my heart and always would, but I had made room for my new husband and father of my Bess. Ward knew loss, and accepted my struggles with losing those close to me. For this, I loved him even more.

When the snow flowers appeared, we were ready to return to our Longhouse. Our family was one less, but the children were growing and their possessions grew with them. When the time came to move from one place to the next, we were always ready for the new season of moons. Each season has three moons: Three high and bright cold moons, three soft moons of re-growth, three moons of much warmth, and three moons to gather and prepare. All moons together were a rule of life that we understood and prepared for, when we worked together with mother earth. She then tended to our needs. When we angered her, she sent upon the people a punishment. We tried hard not to anger her, but as children, we do disappoint at times. Our lives were simple, yet hard.

We tried to find the good in all we saw and to understand the ways that were not the same as ours. Through this we could better understand and survive. Listen, daughters of the future, and learn from the mistakes of all. My heart was sad for the time it would take to right the smallest of wrongs that had been sent upon us by the white man. But, my heart would surely sing with joy for the happening of this day. Are you listening, my granddaughters, as I speak to you through the mist of time? For where only one drop of my blood mixes, you are of mine and I exist so you may exist and you exist because I first existed. Are you listening?

Many of the young maidens – and even our widows - were drawn to the light- skinned men. Many married, as I did, and were drawn to live in the white man's world. Others chose to stay with our People. Each must figure out their own way, my daughters.

I feared for Ward at times as we had much trouble with others moving onto our lands and the game became hard to find. We did not wish to eat the white man's buffalo, but some of our people had no choice. Ward was a trapper by trade, so we were able to fill our pots with this game, but many of the people had to eat of this buffalo meat.

Our hunters had to go further and further from our towns to hunt and many did not return. The paths that we had used for so long were suddenly being used by others. Little Fellow's love for hunting worried me as he traveled so far from home. I myself taught him to hunt the way his father would have. There were places around my Chota that allowed the young to hunt small game close to the homes of their mothers because this was our time to teach them how to care for themselves when they go off hunting or warring.

Time moved so quickly, I soon watched my son grow and become a young warrior. Little Fellow was so similar to his father; I recognized Kingfisher in his looks as well as in the way of his movements. Kingfisher was surely proud of his son and I knew he stayed close to us all in spirit.

Kati had caught the eye of a young soldier and I believed she would wish to marry him by the white way. My heart was glad for her, for the love she had for him shined in her eyes the way mine once shown for her father.

My children were growing up so fast. Little Bess was always trying to keep up with the older two. They loved her so, but life was taking them in other directions. Soon, she would only have her father and me for most of the time. I hoped they would not go far from me, but I knew that soon life would lead them on their own paths.

For a long time now, Fort Loudoun had been one of the strongholds for King George II. With the inevitable passing of both Chief Attakullakulla and Oconostota, it was harder for us to negotiate with the whites. My People were always fearful of the different ways of the Unaka. The British, French, Spanish, New Americans, all have ways that differ from ours. How could we exist with so many different people wanting our lands? Long have I told all who would listen not to sell or trade lands with any of these foreigners. Attakullakulla and I long ago saw where this was leading our People.

Many times I left Chota, or sent one of my trusted ones, to warn those who were in danger. Fear not, I would always protect my own, but in order for our people to stay here we had to get along and live in peace with these people of other lands. My warnings were to protect the lives of my people from the vengeance that could come where I could not intercede. There were those of my clan who will not be glad of this, but what I do was done for their children as well as my own. The seeds we planted, grew, and tended to must live on far into the future.

My heart broke for the things that would come, but my actions would protect our seeds for many, many generations to come. Our blood will mix well with that of the white man's blood, as I saw in little Bess.

When she was but a little over five years old, her father was forced to leave Chota to go east to South Carolina where it was safer for him. These years of travel were dangerous, but as long as I got Bryant into Chota, he was safe. There were safe places all over our lands, and if you were lucky enough to make it to these places, you would not be harmed. This held true for anyone. White, black, or red you were safe in designated areas.

As Bess grew older, she traveled to visit her father more and I had all but stopped going. Ward now had another family. My fondness for him did not leave, but because he lived so far away, his life veered in another direction. At times, I met him along with his new family. I was well accepted by them, and even enjoyed the time we could have together. I was still needed by my People and would be for as long as I live.

I never regret my time spent with Bryant Ward for he taught me so much in our time together. How could I resent him or his new family? I knew Ward's heart, and if circumstances allowed it, he would still be among us. Because I gave my blessing for the union of my husband to a new woman, we all got along well when Bess or I visited him and his new family at their farm in South Carolina.

Bryant helped me with my English as well. My skills were much improved by understanding the language spoken by the Whites. The years of negotiating with the Unaka were seemingly better. All of this helped to serve my People in the best way I knew how.

Bess needed her father in her life, and the road ahead would be hard, but Ward was close enough to our village to travel there easily. Our daughter was still a young one and it was a joy to watch her play cheerfully with the other children. Each time Bryant returned from a trip, he brought her new things to play with. I knew he was proud of his offspring. His kindness was also given to my other children, even though they knew he was not their father, they respect him as such.

As is the custom of our people, my brother, The Raven acted as Kati and Little Fellow's father. The uncle becomes the father, the same way Attakullakulla and Oconostota became fathers to me in my youth after my father died.

Our connection stayed strong over the years because of children. Bryant's son, John Ward, sailed from his home land of Ireland in search of his father and ended up settling in Chota and marrying into my clan. It's funny how this large world seems so small sometimes. Only later did he find his father in South Carolina and eventually settled there. Our time together was so precious; he called me "mother" and my heart sang with every syllable he spoke in love. I would never grow tired of hearing that name.

The Raven and Dragging Canoe were still set strongly against the loss of our lands. Because Chiefs Attakullakulla and Oconostota died so closely to one another, they took their places as new, young Chiefs. They were not afraid to fight whoever they had to in order to hold onto our lands. I saw the despair of the other clans and towns who had to continue to sell, trade, and negotiate with their lands. We held as much of Chota as we could, but even this was becoming harder to do. However I knew if my family had anything to do with it, we would not give up so easily.

Long Fellow settled by the Ocoee River and many times has asked me to move closer to him. I resisted, but knew the time could come when I would have to leave my beloved home of Chota.

The Great Mountain that we called Lookout Mountain was a stronghold to whoever controlled it. For as long as time is, we looked at our enemies from this site. We waged many wars to keep this land. The Unaka used this area also to watch for movements into the land around it.

My People had many sacred places in the surrounding lands. Red Clay, where the Council met, was also a sacred land. A mystic spring came from the ground. The water was pure and cold. The sacred fire was continually burning there. Each year, by ritual, we re-started the fires of our longhouses with ambers from this flame.

When the Unaka came to our land, they did not know how to survive on our lands. We did our best and taught them how to live here. Then, when they no longer needed us, they began to kill us off so they could utilize the land and animals for themselves. I saw there was no end to this and my soul cried out in pain for the suffering of my people.

We just wanted to stay on our lands and live amongst them. Why could this not be? We negotiated with the English, the French, the New Americans, and other tribes. But in the end, we did what we must to survive. Before he died, Attakullakulla traded our lands, sold our lands, and did what had to be done to protect us so we could have a future, despite his best efforts of holding on. Oconostota followed suit for the sake of his People and fought many wars to keep the village safe and hold onto our sacred grounds from those that would harm us. The Creator knew the actions we would take, and prepared paths for us to follow, to wage war upon, and to live upon. My life, my husbands, and my many names were foretold in the stars. I just had a choice to be a part of it on this great and wonderful plan.

Grandmother

Seeds of womb, descendants of my bloodline, listen. I tell you these things through the smoke of time to remind you of your ancestry, of the great Creator, and of the duty we have to the land we so love.

You see my Grandchildren, it has always been hard for me to see into my own future and have the knowing. This is why I share my story, so you can better know your past to propel you into the future.

The Creator leads us. As hard as it is to do, we must trust the guidance given. This is the Creator's wish.

Could the Great Spirit change things that are to be? Yes He can. Will He? Maybe; but maybe not. Do we always understand the plan of the Creator? Most times we do not. Should we trust the Creator? Yes, always. Do we always trust the Great Spirit? No, we were given the will to choose our own path, and yet He loves us.

The way of the One He sent to earth was of pure love. He came to teach all of his love. Later in my life I came to call this man Jesus. The Great Spirit, God, Father, Son, Holy Spirit.

People must believe as they will. It is what makes our own sprit what we want it to be. We are all taught that when we leave this world we go to join the Creator, God.

My spirit told me to do what must be done to ensure that our People live far into the smoke of time. There are those who have judged me in this time and the time that I walked in this land of America. My work was long, sometimes impossible, but my life had purpose. I tried to ensure my land for the future of my beautiful children, grandchildren, and my great grandchildren. My voice I raised for peace. My life I lived to protect my seed for the future. My grandchildren have the hearts of warriors in a time that needs warriors. I longed to see our land survive far into the future of this earth.

Our Mother Earth is tired. We have pulled much from her body. We have put little back. The children and mothers are being poisoned by the land and all that has been poured into our precious water.

When the people of this land decide to change their ways, it should be our ways that they seek. One person can make a difference; one action will lead to another. All must relearn to love this land. We must all forgive the past of a wild wonderful country that grew as was always meant to be. My People and others taught the visitors to our lands how to survive. This they did. People were bought and sold to grow this country. Was it right? No. Many people, white, black, and red lost their lives fighting to change this way. Forgiveness for all races is the way this America will survive, my children.

The Native Americans, pure of blood, and the ones whom have one drop of native blood are the true blood of this land; we have survived thousands of years. The Cherokee and other Nations have told our stories by the fires of their lodges to help this land today and far into the smoke of time.

We will never forget the smoke of the past but forgive we must. All the Native Americans together can make much happen for this land. Again, we will be called to teach the old ways, to care for our earth, for it is the will of the Creator.

Many of the tribes of the first people have been used by all invaders of America. The Navajo from the West were taken as slaves. They were put to the front of the war lines to fight their battles for them. This was to slay more of our own people and to take more land and lessen our numbers as well as the other Nations.

My words are simple for all to understand. Those who listen can hear my cry for peace. And love. And together we will do much.

I can see a time coming, if the story does not change and the red and white hearts do not beat as one, the time will come when we will all be forgotten.

My grandchildren do not grieve for me for my life has been so full, filled with love, pain, sadness, as well as joyous times of pure happiness. I fulfilled my destiny, as well as you must find and fulfill yours.

My light will return when my people come together again as one. For the white man will continue to tear us apart because they know we are weaker when we are separated. True peace will once again rule our Nation when one of my seeds comes to rule. Through his or her eyes, all will see a vision of peace amongst our people and a new day will come to pass and this peace will reign for 100 years.

All red people must then join as one to regain our pride and spirit once more. The time will come when this land will look to us to recall the rhythm of the Mother, our earth. We will be able to help repair her ground and air if they will now listen to the wisdom our Creator has laid upon our hearts and given our charge. Lay down our weapons, and unite in peace as we must grow as one. For if not, the evil will destroy all good the Creator has given all of his children. For when we join with the Creator, we will have much surprise as to who we see on the other side.

Remember these words for they are true.

Love starts in your longhouse and with care it will blossom like the wild rose and spread for all of Creation throughout time.

The End

Timeline

Moytoy

1690 – 1761. *Nanyehi's Grandfather*
Names throughout history: Amatayoa, Amgedohi, Fire King, Old Hop, Kanagatoga, Standing Turkey, Principal Chief, Emperor.
Married Sugi in 1709.

Su Gi

1694 - March 1752. *Nanyehi's Grandmother*
Empress mother of Kati, the one who tames deer or best known as Tame Doe. English name: Catherine.
Married Moytoy in 1709.

Ocanostoa

January 1712 – May 1782. Ogansto, *Nanyehi's Uncle*
War Chief who married Lucy Ward, lady in waiting to Queen of England.

Attakullakulla

December 1712 – 1782. *Nanyehi's Uncle*
Little Carpenter, Little Sausage, Peace Chief, The Carpenter, Little Prince

Dragging Canoe

1732 – 1792. *Nanyehi's cousin*

Son of Attakullakulla ,War Chief, Little Owl, Tsi yu Gansi hi.

Tame Doe

December 1712 – 1806. *Nanyehi's Mother*

Catherine Fivekiller, Tame Deer.

Fivekiller

DOB ? – 1738 *Nanyehi's Father*

Skayagustuegwo, Bird Clan

Longfellow

1734 - 1835. *Nanyehi's Brother.*

Tuskeegeeteehee, Raven of Chota, The Raven.

Nancy Ward

November 14, 1738 – 1822.

Named at birth: Tsistuna-gis-ke`, Wild Rose, Nanyehi, Nanaha, Ghighau, Chiconehla.

Kingfisher

1736 – 1755. *Nanyehi's first Husband*

Tsu-la, died in the battle of Taliwa, Ball Ground, Canton County, Georgia.

Catherine Kingfisher

April 1753 – 1828. *Nanyehi's Daughter*

Little Kati, married three times and had 10 children.

Hiskyteehee

1755 – 1835. *Nanyehi's Son*

Little Fellow, Raven of Chota, The Raven, Private Morgan

American name: Pathkiller.

Married and had no surviving children.

Lucy Ward

DOB ? – 1744. *Cousin to Bryant Ward*

Married Oconostoa. Lady in waiting to Queen of England. Died in Chota of small pox that scared her husband.

Bryant Ward

1714 – 1809. *Nanyehi's second Husband* and father of Elizabeth Ward. Also referred to as Bryan Ward.

Elizabeth Ward

1759 – 1793. *Nanyehi's Daughter*

Bess, Betsy

Married with 3 children.

Murdered in John Beards Raid.

John Ward

1734 – 1820. *Nanyehi's Step-Son*

Married second cousin of Nancy Ward.

Born in Ireland to an Irishwoman, Bryant's first wife.

CPSIA information can be obtained
at www.ICGtesting.com
Printed in the USA
BVHW052041221122
652525BV00013B/828/J

9 781943 496082